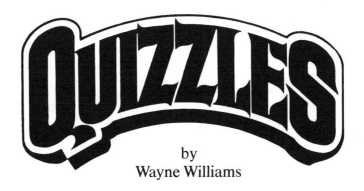

by
Wayne Williams

A resource for developing logic skills

Ace Books

A Division of Charter Communications, Inc.

A GROSSET & DUNLAP COMPANY

Educational Edition

Produced by

DALE
SEYMOUR
PUBLICATIONS
P.O. BOX 10888
PALO ALTO, CA 94303

Educational Edition designed by Dale Seymour Publications
Exclusive license to publish granted to Dale Seymour Publications
by Charter Communications, Inc.

Copyright © 1976 by Grosset & Dunlap, Inc.
Published simultaneously in Canada
Printed in the United States of America
First Ace Printing: July, 1981
Dale Seymour Publications Printing: February, 1982

ISBN 0-86651-102-4

Order Number DS01285

defghi-MA-8765

PROBLEM SOLVING WITH QUIZZLES

The National Council of Teachers of Mathematics, an organization of professional educators, recommends that the number one priority for the 1980s for mathematics teachers is to make problem solving the focus of their instruction.

Problem solving includes a broad range of strategies. One of the important strategies for solving problems is deductive logic. This strategy is often the only one needed to solve a problem. This book presents a number of problems using this particular strategy.

How to Use This Book

The problems in this edition of QUIZZLES are especially designed as student worksheets. They were made to be duplicated. Limited reproduction permission is granted to provide a classroom set of materials. This book solves a sample quizzle step-by-step so you can give your students ideas about how to use the clue charts.

The type and charts are large—sufficiently large for over-head transparency use with class-developed lessons. Also, the quizzle solutions can be put on a chart and presented on the overhead.

It is not likely that any class will solve all 38 quizzles. As the puzzle numbers increase, the puzzles become more difficult. You may decide to use the later puzzles as enrichment exercises for your gifted students or students who particularly enjoy logic problems.

WELCOME TO QUIZZLES

Because Quizzles are logic problems, and because people think differently, there are many routes to the one correct answer to each quizzle.

We have included a clue chart with each quizzle in this book. The chart will help you to record what you learn from each clue and also to record the facts that can be *deduced* by putting two or more clues together. Here is how to use the clue chart:

Suppose a clue told you: TWO BOYS HAD DIFFERENT MEATS FOR DINNER. JOHN DID NOT HAVE HAM. You would put an "x" (meaning "no") on the chart, where John's row crosses the "ham" column, like this:

	HAM	BEEF
JOHN	X	
JIM		

Now suppose the clue had told you: TWO BOYS HAD DIFFERENT MEATS. JIM HAD HAM. You would put an "O" (meaning "yes") where Jim's row crosses the "ham" column. You could also deduce from this that if Jim had the ham, John *did not*. So an "x" goes in John's "ham" box. Also, if Jim had ham, you can deduce that he did not have beef—so still another "x" goes on the chart, where the "beef" column crosses Jim's row. The remaining space gets an "O." John must have had beef!

	HAM	BEEF
JOHN	X	O
JIM	O	X

Of course, this little quizzle is so simple, it's hardly a puzzle at all. Still the principle and use of the clue chart is the same as for the more challenging quizzles in this book.

HOW TO SOLVE QUIZZLES—STEP BY STEP

Quizzles are reasoning puzzles. Each puzzle has a set-up, a set of clues, and a clue-chart to help you plot the facts as you go.

To give you the hang of it, let's solve a sample Quizzle. Here's the set-up:

DOUBLE STARS

There are five films playing in town, a comedy, a western, a thriller, a mystery, and a sci-fi film. Each of the films stars a different leading man. They are Peter O'Toole, Dirk Bogarde, Clint Eastwood, Charlton Heston, and Laurence Olivier. As it happens, each of the films also stars a different leading lady. The female stars are Faye Dunaway, Julie Christie, Jacqueline Bisset, Liz Taylor, and Shirley MacLaine. From the clues given try to determine the male and female lead in each type of film.

Here are the clues:

1. Neither Charlton Heston nor Laurence Olivier star in the western but one stars with Jacqueline Bisset and the other with Faye Dunaway.
2. Julie Christie stars in the mystery but not with Clint Eastwood.
3. The sci-fi film does not star Jacqueline Bisset.
4. Peter O'Toole is not in a film with Shirley MacLaine and neither of them are in a mystery, sci-fi, or comedy film.
5. Charlton Heston is not in the comedy and Peter O'Toole is not in the western.

Here is the clue chart:

	COMEDY	WESTERN	THRILLER	MYSTERY	SCI-FI	DUNAWAY	CHRISTIE	BISSET	TAYLOR	MACLAINE
O'TOOLE										
BOGARDE										
EASTWOOD										
HESTON										
OLIVIER										
DUNAWAY										
CHRISTIE										
BISSET										
TAYLOR										
MACLAINE										

Let's solve this Quizzle clue by clue. We'll use the clue chart to record what we *know* and what we *deduce* from each clue.

The best attack is to take each clue in order and see what it tells you about each item in the puzzle and its relationship to other items. For instance, in clue 1, we'll learn things about Charlton Heston *and* about his relationship to two other groups of items, actresses and kinds of movies.

Look at clue 1:

1. Neither Charlton Heston nor Laurence Olivier star in the western but one stars with Jacqueline Bisset and the other with Faye Dunaway.

The clue states that Charlton Heston is *not* in a western film, so put an 'x' in the western column where it crosses the Heston row.

The clue also states that Heston stars with either Bisset or Dunaway. From this we can deduce that he *does not* star with Christie, Taylor, or MacLaine. So now we put three more 'x's on the chart, where Christie, Taylor, and MacLaine's columns cross the Heston row. We know the same about Laurence Olivier, so we can put the appropriate marks on the chart. At this point, we have charted all the *stated* facts in the clue. The chart will look like this:

	COMEDY	WESTERN	THRILLER	MYSTERY	SCI-FI	DUNAWAY	CHRISTIE	BISSET	TAYLOR	MACLAINE
O'TOOLE										
BOGARDE										
EASTWOOD										
HESTON		X					X		X	X
OLIVIER		X					X		X	X
DUNAWAY										
CHRISTIE										
BISSET										
TAYLOR										
MACLAINE										

Now we must deduce some information. We have already put 'x's on the chart to show that Olivier and Heston are not in the

vi

western. We can deduce that Bisset and Dunaway cannot be in the western either — because they star with Heston and Olivier (who aren't in a western). So two more 'x's go on the chart, where the western column crosses the rows for Bisset and Dunaway.

Taking things one step further — if Bisset and Dunaway star with Heston and Olivier, then Bisset and Dunaway *do not* star with O'Toole, Bogarde, or Eastwood. So six new 'x's go on your chart — where the Bisset and Dunaway columns cross the O'Toole, Bogarde, and Eastwood rows.

See how much you learned from one simple clue? At this point, your chart should look like this:

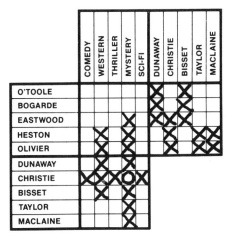

Let's move on to clue 2:

2. Julie Christie stars in the mystery but not with Clint Eastwood.

Aha! Julie Christie stars in the mystery. That means we put an 'O' where the mystery column crosses the Julie Christie row.

If Christie stars in the mystery, the other four actresses do not — so four 'x's go in the mystery column where it crosses the rows of Dunaway, Bisset, Taylor, and MacLaine. Also, if Julie Christie stars in the mystery, we deduce that she *does not* star in any other kind of film. So four more 'x's go on the chart: where Julie Christie's row crosses the comedy, thriller, western, and sci-fi columns.

Important: whenever there is a 'O' in a space, you can put X's in the remaining spaces in that row and column within THE SQUARE.

The clue also tells us that Clint Eastwood *did not* star in the mystery with Julie Christie. That means two more 'x's: one where Eastwood's row crosses the mystery column and one where it crosses the Christie column.

Now, to get the next bit of information, we must put clues 1 and 2 together. In clue 1, we learned that Heston and Olivier did not star with Julie Christie. In clue 2, we learned that Christie starred in the mystery — THEREFORE, Heston and Olivier could not have starred in the mystery! Put the two appropriate x's on your chart. The chart will now look like this:

Clue 3 is a snap:

3. The sci-fi film does not star Jacqueline Bisset.

Just put an 'x' where the sci-fi column crosses the Bisset row.

Clue 4 is more complicated.

4. Peter O'Toole is not in a film with Shirley MacLaine and neither of them are in a mystery, sci-fi, or comedy film.

Let's start by seeing what the clue tells us about Peter O'Toole. First, he is *not* in a film with Shirley MacLaine, so we can put an 'x' where his row crosses her column. Second, he is *not* in a mystery, sci-fi, or comedy film. Three more 'x's go on the chart. Now the chart looks like this:

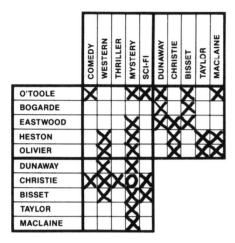

Study the chart for a moment. You will notice that all of the actor boxes in the mystery column are filled *except* for Bogarde's. That means that Bogarde is the only actor who could have starred in the mystery. So you can now put an 'O' in the mystery column where it crosses Bogarde's row.

Also, if Bogarde starred in a mystery he couldn't have starred in any other kind of film; put 'x's where the Bogarde row crosses the columns for comedy, western, sci-fi, and thriller.

At this point, the mystery column shows that Christie and Bogarde starred in the mystery. Because they appeared *together* in the mystery, you can put an 'O' where Bogarde's row crosses Christie's column. If he starred with Christie, he did *not* star with anyone else. That means two x's go where Bogarde's row crosses the Taylor and MacLaine columns. (His Dunaway and Bisset boxes are already 'x'ed from clue 1.) Likewise, the Christie column now gets an 'x' in O'Toole's row (the column's only remaining empty space). She couldn't have starred with O'Toole because she starred

with Bogarde! Now your chart should look like this:

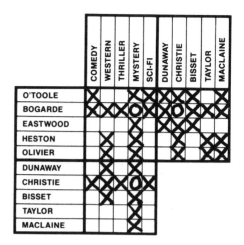

Look at the chart again—hard. Did you notice that the Shirley MacLaine column shows that she *does not* star with O'Toole, Bogarde, Heston, or Olivier, and that she has only one box left open? This means she *must have* starred with Eastwood. Put an 'O' where her column crosses his row. Put an 'x' in the remaining box of Eastwood's actress row. (If he starred with MacLaine, he *could not have* starred with anyone else).

Important: whenever there are four 'x's in a row or column WITHIN A SQUARE, you can put an 'O' in the remaining space.

Look at the chart closely again. Do you see the other hidden fact? The O'Toole row has 'X's in the Dunaway, Christie, Bisset, and MacLaine columns.

This means he can only have starred with the remaining lady — Elizabeth Taylor, the one whose box is empty in his row. Put an 'O' there.

Whenever you have an 'O', you can usually use it to deduce some new information. In this case, we just found out that O'Toole stars with Liz Taylor. Look at his row. He can only have starred in a western or a thriller. What does that tell us about Taylor? That *she* can only have starred in a western or a thriller *too*. So in Taylor's row, we can put x's in every film box *except* the western and thriller. (We already knew she did not star in the mystery.) The chart now looks like this:

	COMEDY	WESTERN	THRILLER	MYSTERY	SCI-FI	DUNAWAY	CHRISTIE	BISSET	TAYLOR	MACLAINE
O'TOOLE	X			X	X	X	X	X	O	X
BOGARDE	X	O	X	O		X	X	X	X	X
EASTWOOD				X		X	X	X	X	X
HESTON			X							
OLIVIER			X				X	X		X
DUNAWAY					X					
CHRISTIE		X	X	X	O	X				
BISSET		X								
TAYLOR		X		X						
MACLAINE					X					

Remember Clue 4? It went like this:

4. Peter O'Toole is not in a film with Shirley MacLaine and neither of them are in a mystery, sci-fi, or comedy film.

We've already looked at this clue as it related to Peter O'Toole. Now let's see what it says about Shirley MacLaine. Simple. She was not in the mystery, sci-fi, or comedy films. So x's go in those columns, in her row. We found out a moment ago that MacLaine *stars* with Eastwood, so we can put 'x's in his mystery, sci-fi, and comedy columns too.

Now look hard and see if you can find a new piece of hidden information. Right. There is now an 'x' in every actress box of the sci-fi column *except* where it crosses Faye Dunaway's row. So put an 'O' where the Dunaway row and sci-fi column meet. Faye Dunaway was in the sci-fi film! That means she can't have been in any other kind of film, so 'x's go in the remaining film boxes in Faye's row.

If you look hard after putting in the last information, you'll see that actress boxes of the comedy column are now full, except the Jacqueline Bisset box. So Bisset was in the comedy! Put in another 'O'! Bisset can't have been in anything else, so an 'x' goes in the thriller column in Bisset's row. (That's the only open box in her film row, anyway.)

At this point, the chart should look like this:

	COMEDY	WESTERN	THRILLER	MYSTERY	SCI-FI	DUNAWAY	CHRISTIE	BISSET	TAYLOR	MACLAINE
O'TOOLE	X			X	X	X	X	X	O	X
BOGARDE	X	X	O	X		X	O	X	X	X
EASTWOOD	X			X	X	X	X	X	X	O
HESTON		X								
OLIVIER		X				X	X	X		X
DUNAWAY	X	X	X	X	O					
CHRISTIE	X	X	X	O	X					
BISSET	O	X	X	X	X					
TAYLOR	X		X	X						
MACLAINE	X		X	X	X					

Now we're getting somewhere. Let's see if we can use the 'O's we just put in to dig up some new information. Dunaway is in the sci-fi and Bisset is in the comedy. We know from clue 1 (and from looking at the chart) that Heston and Olivier are in films with Dunaway and Bisset, although we still don't know who is with whom. Still, if they are with Dunaway and Bisset, who are in either the comedy or sci-fi, Heston and Olivier are in either the comedy or the sci-fi too. We have already put 'x's in the Heston and O'Toole mystery and western boxes, but now we can put 'x's in their thriller boxes as well. Why? To repeat, they're with Bisset and Dunaway — and Bisset and Dunaway are in the comedy and sci-fi, *not* in the thriller. Put in these two x's and let's move on to clue five:

5. Charlton Heston is not in the comedy and Peter O'Toole is not in the western.

Aha, again! Heston isn't in the comedy! So put an 'x' in his row in the comedy column. This leaves only Olivier to be the star of the comedy, so we can put an 'O' in the Olivier row, where it crosses the comedy column, and two 'x's where the Olivier row crosses the thriller and sci-fi columns.

Looking hard at the chart once more, we see that Heston's is now the only open box under sci-fi — so Heston is in the sci-fi film and an 'O' goes there.

We already know that Faye Dunaway is in the sci-fi film. Now we know that Heston

ix

is too. So Dunaway and Heston are together! Put an 'O' in *her* column, where it crosses his row and an 'x' where either of them crosses anyone else.

Do the same thing for Bisset and Olivier. (We just found out that Olivier is in the comedy. We already knew that Bisset is too. So Bisset and Olivier are together. Put an 'O' in her column, where it crosses his row and an 'x' where either of them crosses anyone else).

Now, your chart looks like this:

	COMEDY	WESTERN	THRILLER	MYSTERY	SCI-FI	DUNAWAY	CHRISTIE	BISSET	TAYLOR	MACLAINE
O'TOOLE	X			X	X	X	X	X	O	X
BOGARDE	X	X	X	O	X	X	O	X	X	X
EASTWOOD	X			X	X	X	X	X	X	O
HESTON	X	X	X	X	O	O	X	X	X	X
OLIVIER	O	X	X	X	X	X	X	O	X	X
DUNAWAY	X	X	X	X	O					
CHRISTIE	X	X	X	O	X					
BISSET	O	X	X	X	X					
TAYLOR	X			X	X					
MACLAINE	X			X	X					

We're really down to the home stretch. All we need to know is the types of films the O'Toole-Taylor team and Eastwood MacLaine team are in. The only two types of film left are the western and the thriller. Clue 5 says in no uncertain terms that Peter O'Toole is *not* in the western. That means that O'Toole is *in the thriller*. Taylor is with O'Toole, so both get "O"'s in their thriller boxes, and "X"'s in the remaining boxes. This leaves the western to be the film starring Eastwood and MacLaine. Put in the appropriate "O"'s — and you've solved your first Quizzle!

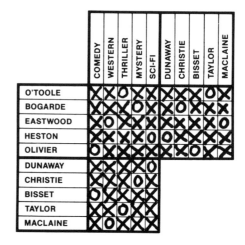

1. FIVE BOYS AND FIVE DOGS

Eric, Bernard, Bart, Sidney, and Ralph have dogs named (in no particular order) Bowser, Fido, Rover, Snoopy, and Spot. These five dogs are (again in no particular order) a poodle, a basset, a terrier, a spaniel and a collie. From the clues given try to determine the name and the breed of each boy's dog.

1. No dog's name begins with the same letter as that of his master.
2. Rover is not Bart's or Sidney's dog.
3. Spot's master and the owner of the spaniel both have names beginning with the same letter.
4. Neither Eric's dog nor Bernard's dog is the basset, nor is Snoopy.
5. Bart's dog and the collie are not called Spot or Snoopy.
6. Ralph's dog is not a terrier.

	POODLE	BASSET	TERRIER	SPANIEL	COLLIE	BOWSER	FIDO	ROVER	SNOOPY	SPOT
ERIC										
BERNARD										
BART										
SIDNEY										
RALPH										
BOWSER					
FIDO					
ROVER					
SNOOPY					
SPOT					

1

2. FIVE WOMEN OUT TO DINNER

Some women from the District Attorney's office went out to dinner last night. Elizabeth, Gladys, Barbara, Virginia and Gwendolyn were their names, and each ordered a different main course. Steak, ham, chicken, pork, and lamb were the only main courses on the menu. Each woman also ordered mashed potatoes, salad, and a different vegetable. The five vegetables on the menu were peas, carrots, corn, squash, and spinach. What main course and vegetable did each woman have?

1. The woman who had steak and corn sat on the left of Elizabeth and on the right of Gwendolyn.
2. The woman who had chicken doesn't play cards but the woman who had ham, the woman who had squash, and Barbara played bridge yesterday with Gwendolyn.
3. The woman who had squash did not have it with pork; Virginia did not order pork either.
4. The woman who had ham was recently married to Elizabeth's brother; the woman who had squash helped Elizabeth wrap her present.
5. Gladys's and Gwendolyn's vegetables begin with the same letter as do the vegetables of Elizabeth and Barbara.

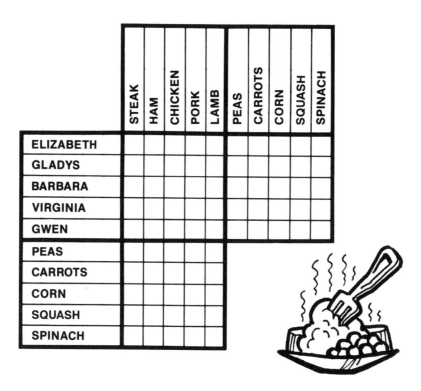

	STEAK	HAM	CHICKEN	PORK	LAMB	PEAS	CARROTS	CORN	SQUASH	SPINACH
ELIZABETH										
GLADYS										
BARBARA										
VIRGINIA										
GWEN										
PEAS										
CARROTS										
CORN										
SQUASH										
SPINACH										

3. PARKING LOT

Mr. Smith, Mr. Jones, Mr. Brown, Mr. Johnson, and Mr. Black work for the Tinyburg Electric Company. Their cars are different colors: red, yellow, green, blue, and white. As it happens, each man also drives a different type of car: a sedan, a station wagon, a sports car, a coupe, and a convertible. From the clues given try to determine the owner, color, and type of each car.

1. Neither Mr. Johnson nor Mr. Jones owns the red car, but one of them owns the convertible.
2. Mr. Jones, Mr. Brown, and the owner of the sedan sometimes go on camping trips with the owner of the yellow station wagon.
3. The coupe and the white car are owned by the men with the colorful last names.
4. Mr. Smith used to own the sports car but then he changed its original white color and sold it to one of the other men who did not paint it green.
5. Mr. Johnson owns a green car.

	SMITH	JONES	BROWN	JOHNSON	BLACK	RED	YELLOW	GREEN	BLUE	WHITE
SEDAN										
STA. WAGON										
SPORTS CAR										
COUPE										
CONVERT.										
RED										
YELLOW										
GREEN										
BLUE										
WHITE										

4. WHO DUN ITS

One rainy evening, five military men were murdered in the old mansion on Willow Lane (a general, a captain, a lieutenant, a sergeant, and a corporal). The murders took place in the bedroom, basement, pantry, den, and attic of the house. No two men were murdered in the same room or with the same weapon. The weapons used were poison, a poker, a gun, a knife, and a shovel. From the clues given, try to determine the room in which each man was killed and the weapon used to do him in.

1. The murder with the shovel was not done in the den or the attic; neither the captain nor the lieutenant was killed with the shovel, nor was either killed in the den or the attic.
2. The captain was not murdered in the bedroom.
3. The poker was not the murder weapon used in the attic.
4. Neither the general nor the corporal was murdered with poison, a gun, or a shovel.
5. The man murdered in the basement was not the corporal or the captain nor was he the man done in with poison or the poker.

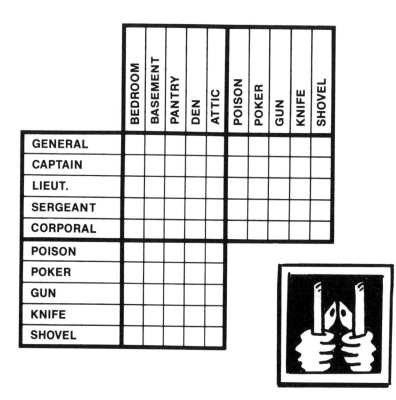

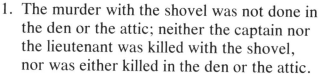
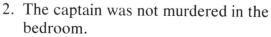

5. VISITING RELATIVES

During his summer vacation, John decided to visit some of his relatives—his cousin, his parents, his uncle, his nephew and his brother —who all live in different cities. The five cities they live in are St. Louis, Denver, Miami, San Francisco, and Boston. John used five different means of transportation to get from one city to another. He went by car, plane, bus, train, and motorcycle. From the clues given, try to determine the city in which each of his relatives live and the means of transportation John used to reach there.

1. He arrived by plane and bus at the two cities which are not on the coast.
2. His uncle and his cousin live on the east coast.
3. His nephew met his plane when he arrived.
4. He did not arrive at his uncle's city by car and his uncle does not live in Boston.
5. He did not go by bus to St. Louis or to visit his parents and he did not go to his cousin's city by train or car.

	COUSIN	PARENTS	UNCLE	NEPHEW	BROTHER	CAR	PLANE	BUS	TRAIN	CYCLE
ST. LOUIS										
DENVER										
MIAMI										
S.F.										
BOSTON										
CAR										
PLANE										
BUS										
TRAIN										
CYCLE										

ARRIVED BY

6. FAMILY AT HOME

Each member of the Smith family—
father, mother, daughter, son and aunt—
is in a different room doing something.
One is reading, one is writing a letter, one is
watching T.V., one is on the telephone, and one
is doing a crossword puzzle. The five rooms in
which these activities are taking place are the
living room, the dining room, a bedroom, the
kitchen, and the den. Where is each family
member and what is he or she doing?

1. Someone is reading in the living room.
2. Neither of the men is the person in the dining room or the person on the telephone but
   one of them is in the bedroom.
3. The person doing the crossword puzzle oc-
   casionally calls out for help with a clue to
   the person in the living room and the aunt.
4. The person in the den is not one of the women and is not writing, nor are
   the women writing the letter.
5. One of the parents is watching T.V. and one of the children is doing the
   crossword.
6. The person in the den is not doing a crossword puzzle.

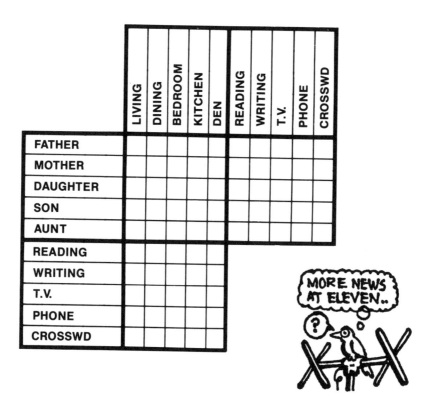

	LIVING	DINING	BEDROOM	KITCHEN	DEN	READING	WRITING	T.V.	PHONE	CROSSWD
FATHER										
MOTHER										
DAUGHTER										
SON										
AUNT										
READING										
WRITING										
T.V.										
PHONE										
CROSSWD										

MORE NEWS AT ELEVEN..

7. NIGHT CLASSES

Pamela, Dorothy, Rita, Eunice, and Bernice are each taking an art course and a foreign language course. The art courses are painting, drawing, sculpture, pottery, and graphics. The foreign languages are French, Italian, Spanish, German, and Chinese. From the clues given try to determine the art course and the language course each woman is taking.

1. The woman taking sculpture is not taking Italian.
2. Bernice and Pamela do not study Chinese but one takes pottery, and the other French.
3. The woman studying Italian has taken other courses with Dorothy and Eunice, but she has never had a class with the women taking drawing and pottery.
4. Dorothy does not study German.
5. Bernice, Dorothy, and Eunice drive to class together on Thursday night. In no particular order, one of these women takes graphics, one takes German, and the other one takes pottery.

	PAINTING	DRAWING	SCULPTURE	POTTERY	GRAPHICS	FRENCH	ITALIAN	SPANISH	GERMAN	CHINESE
PAMELA										
DOROTHY										
RITA										
EUNICE										
BERNICE										
FRENCH										
ITALIAN										
SPANISH										
GERMAN										
CHINESE										

8. FORMER HOMES

A group of men live and work in New York City (Mr. Lester, Mr. Becket, Mr. Lennox, Mr. Standish, and Mr. Weiss). Formerly, each had made his home in two other cities. The men lived first in the cities of New Orleans, Seattle, Milwaukee, Denver, and Dallas. They then lived in the cities of San Francisco, Houston, Atlanta, Boston, and Los Angeles. From the clues given, try to determine the two former cities in which each man lived.

1. Mr. Weiss has always lived in the South, but Mr. Standish never has.
2. The man from New Orleans, the man from Denver and Mr. Lester all would have liked to have lived in San Francisco.
3. Mr. Becket has not lived in Milwaukee or New Orleans.
4. Neither Mr. Lennox or Mr. Standish has ever lived in a city with a two-word name.
5. Neither Mr. Lennox nor Mr. Weiss has ever lived on the west coast but one of them has always lived in Texas.

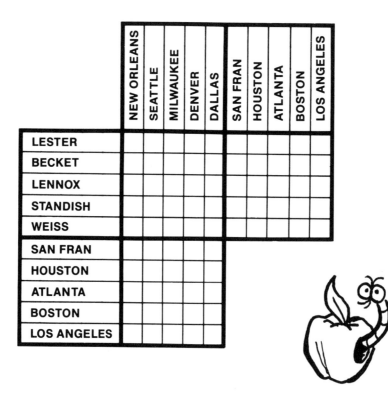

8

9. FAMILY WEDDINGS

Last June, five brothers married five sisters on the same day, in the same church, five different ceremonies. The five brothers are Earl, Virgil, Lester, Leroy, and Ray. The five sisters (and brides) are Betty Lou, Peggy Sue, Mary Jane, Sally Jo, and Cindy Lee. From the clues given, try to determine the composition of each couple and the order in which the ceremonies were performed.

1. Lester was married after Cindy Lee and Mary Jane but before Earl and Leroy.
2. Betty Lou was not Lester's bride.
3. The first and last couples to be married featured Cindy Lee, Sally Jo, Virgil, and Leroy.

	BETTY LOU	PEGGY SUE	MARY JANE	SALLY JO	CINDY LEE	FIRST	SECOND	THIRD	FOURTH	FIFTH
EARL										
VIRGIL										
LESTER										
LEROY										
RAY										
FIRST					
SECOND					
THIRD					
FOURTH					
FIFTH					

10. THE LITTLE BIG TOP

Victor, Virgil, Vincent, Vito, and Vance are brothers performing in a five-man traveling circus known as the Little Big Top. They are, in no particular order, a clown, a juggler, an acrobat, a magician, and a strong man. Whenever they perform, their acts appear in the same order. From the clues given try to determine each brother's act and the order in which they perform.

1. The clown comes on after Victor and Vito but before the magician.
2. The acrobat comes on third.
3. Neither the strong man nor Vincent is the first or last to perform.
4. Virgil, Victor, and Vito perform in that order.

	VICTOR	VIRGIL	VINCENT	VITO	VANCE	FIRST	SECOND	THIRD	FOURTH	FIFTH
CLOWN										
JUGGLER										
ACROBAT										
MAGICIAN										
STRONG MAN										
FIRST					
SECOND					
THIRD					
FOURTH					
FIFTH					

11. A HEIGHT AND HAIR COLOR PROBLEM

Mary, Isobel, Marcia, Grace, and Ruth are on the Grand Avenue Grade School girls' basketball team. Each girl has a different color hair. The hair colors are blond, red, auburn, black, and brunette. As it happens, no two girls on the team are the same height; they are 5'9", 5'8", 5'6", 5'5", and 5'4". From the clues given try to determine the hair color and height of each of the girls on the team.

1. Mary is taller than Ruth who is two inches taller than the redhead.
2. The brunette is not 5'6".
3. Marcia and Mary are neither the tallest nor the shortest.
4. The girl with black hair is two inches taller than Ruth.
5. Isobel is taller than the blond, who is one inch taller than Grace.

	BLOND	RED	AUBURN	BLACK	BRUNETTE	5'9"	5'8"	5'6"	5'5"	5'4"
MARY										
ISOBEL										
MARCIA										
GRACE										
RUTH										
5'9"										
5'8"										
5'6"										
5'5"										
5'4"										

12. FIVE DAUGHTERS' SONS

Between January 1 and May 31, Mrs. Jackson's daughters Jane, Jean, Joan, June, and Jill, gave birth to five sons. The names of the boys, in no particular order, are Leonard, Edward, Harry, Malcolm, and David. What was the name of each daughter's son and in what month was he born? Each daughter gave birth in a different month.

1. Jill's baby was born after Harry and they were both born after Leonard.
2. David was born before Harry but neither David nor Malcolm was born first or last.
3. Joan, Jane, and Jean gave birth in that order.
4. Malcolm, June's son Edward, and the boy born in March all have blond hair.
5. Joan's son is older than both Harry and Malcolm.

	LEONARD	EDWARD	HARRY	MALCOLM	DAVID	JANUARY	FEBRUARY	MARCH	APRIL	MAY
JANE										
JEAN										
JOAN										
JUNE										
JILL										
JANUARY					
FEBRUARY					
MARCH					
APRIL					
MAY					

13. FIVE STREETS CROSS MAIN

Main Street in Smallville is crossed by these other streets: River, Oak, Highland, Northfield, and Evergreen. Each street name is followed by one of the following: Avenue, Boulevard, Road, Lane, or Drive. From the clues given, try to determine the name of each street and the order in which one would cross them if one were coming down Main Street.

1. Evergreen Boulevard is not the first or the last street one would cross.
2. One would cross Evergreen before Oak, which one would cross before the Avenue.
3. The Road comes after the Boulevard but before the Lane and they all come before Highland.
4. River is the middle street.

	AVENUE	BLVD.	ROAD	LANE	DRIVE	FIRST	SECOND	THIRD	FOURTH	FIFTH
RIVER										
OAK										
HIGHLAND										
NORTHFIELD										
EVERGREEN										
FIRST					
SECOND					
THIRD					
FOURTH					
FIFTH					

14. COMMEMORATIVE STAMPS

Edison, Marconi, the Wright Brothers, Franklin, and Bell, are pictured on 5 cent, 10 cent, 15 cent, 20 cent and 25 cent stamps which are red, blue, green, gray, and yellow. Whose picture is on what colored stamp and what is the value of each?

1. The Edison stamp is worth more than the brown one which costs more than the Marconi stamp.
2. The Wright Brothers stamp costs twice as much as the green one.
3. The blue stamp costs less than the Franklin stamp but more than the 15 cent red one.
4. The Edison stamp did not cost 20 cents.

	RED	BLUE	GREEN	GRAY	BROWN	CENTS 5	10	15	20	25
EDISON										
MARCONI										
WRIGHT										
FRANKLIN										
BELL										
CENTS 5										
10						
15						
20						
25						

15. FAMILY FAVORITES

The members of the Jones family—the father, the mother, the daughter, the son, and the aunt —each have a favorite television program. One likes a comedy, one a western, one a drama, one an interview show, and one a sports program. Each of the favorite programs is on a different weeknight. From the clues given try to determine the type of show that is each person's favorite and the night it is on.

1. The comedy is not on Tuesday.
2. None of the women's favorite shows is a sports program or the one on Wednesday night.
3. The mother's favorite show is on earlier in the week than the drama but later than the son's favorite show.
4. One of the parents likes a western and the other likes a show that is on Monday.
5. The daughter does not like the interview show.

	COMEDY	WESTERN	DRAMA	INTERVIEW	SPORTS	MONDAY	TUESDAY	WEDNESDAY	THURSDAY	FRIDAY
FATHER										
MOTHER										
DAUGHTER										
SON										
AUNT										
MONDAY										
TUESDAY										
WEDNESDAY										
THURSDAY										
FRIDAY										

16. TWO WEEKS VACATION

Gardner, Plunkett, Maloney, Phelps, and Lopez work for the Littleville fire department. They each get two weeks vacation per year. As it happens, last year they each took their first week in the first five months of the year and their second week in the last five months of the year. Remembering that each man took each of his weeks in a different month, try to determine the months in which each man took his first and second weeks.

1. Mr. Plunkett took his first week before Mr. Gardner who took his before Mr. Phelps; for their second week the order was reversed.
2. The man who vacationed in March also vacationed in September.
3. Mr. Lopez did not take his first week in April or in March.
4. Neither Mr. Lopez nor the man who took his first week in January took his second week in August or December.
5. Mr. Maloney took his second week before Mr. Plunkett but after Mr. Lopez.

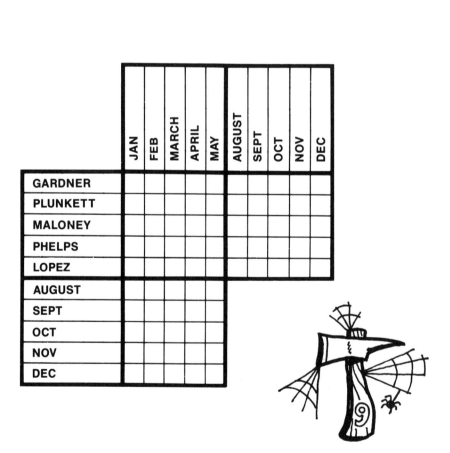

	JAN	FEB	MARCH	APRIL	MAY	AUGUST	SEPT	OCT	NOV	DEC
GARDNER										
PLUNKETT										
MALONEY										
PHELPS										
LOPEZ										
AUGUST										
SEPT										
OCT										
NOV										
DEC										

17. ROYALTY OF THE LAND OF PIRNZ

Among the royalty of the land of Pirnz are Velve, Brint, Draz, Flard, and Sorn. In no particular order, their titles are queen, marquis, duke, baron, and duchess. Their ages are 25, 30, 35, 40, and 45. From the clues given try to determine the age and title of each of the five.

1. Flard is younger than Sorn who is younger than the queen but the duchess is older than all three.
2. Velve is older than the baron who is older than Brint but none of these three is the youngest.
3. Draz is not the oldest, nor is Draz the name of any of the men.
4. Sorn is not 40 years old and neither is the duchess.
5. Brint is not the marquis.

		VELVE	BRINT	DRAZ	FLARD	SORN	AGE				
							45	40	35	30	25
QUEEN											
MARQUIS											
DUKE											
BARON											
DUCHESS											
AGE	45					
	40					
	35					
	30					
	25					

18. SPORTSVILLE TEAMS

There are four stadiums in Sportsville: Memorial, the Coliseum, Central, and All Saints. These are the home grounds for the football, soccer, baseball, tennis, and basketball teams. Two teams share the same stadium. The five teams are the Blazers, the Fireballs, the Streaks, the Flames, and the Demons. From the clues given, try to determine the nickname of each sports team and the stadium at which they play.

1. Neither the Demons nor the team that plays at Central must share its stadium but the Flames must.
2. The football team doesn't play at Central stadium and it shares its stadium with the Streaks.
3. The basketball team, the baseball team, and the Fireballs do not share their stadiums.
4. The soccer team is not called the Fireballs and doesn't play at All Saints.
5. The tennis team plays at Memorial stadium but the baseball team does not play at All Saints.

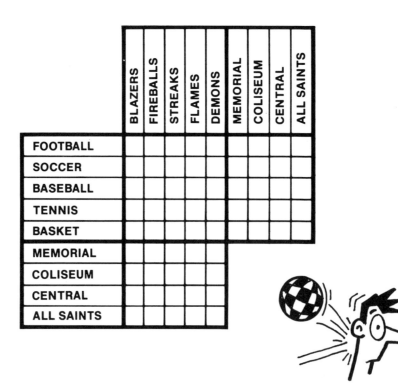

	BLAZERS	FIREBALLS	STREAKS	FLAMES	DEMONS	MEMORIAL	COLISEUM	CENTRAL	ALL SAINTS
FOOTBALL									
SOCCER									
BASEBALL									
TENNIS									
BASKET									
MEMORIAL									
COLISEUM									
CENTRAL									
ALL SAINTS									

19. THE PHOTO CONTEST

There is a photography contest every year at the County Fair. In last year's contest, the top prizes were awarded to photographs of fish, trees, cats, tenements, flowers, and a bridge. Two of the prizes were won by one man. The men who won the top prizes were Mr. Vee, Mr. Kay, Mr. Jay, Mr. Dee, and Mr. X. From the clues given, try to determine who took each photograph and the prize that each picture won.

1. The bridge and tenement photographs were taken by one man and neither picture won first or last prize.
2. The last name of the man who won first prize is alphabetically behind everyone except the man whose photograph is of trees.
3. Neither Mr. Jay's photograph nor the photos of the bridge and the tenement came in third.
4. The tenement photograph, the cat's photograph and Mr. Dee's photograph of flowers finished in that order.
5. The fish photograph received a higher prize than Mr. Jay's photograph which in turn did better than the flowers photograph.

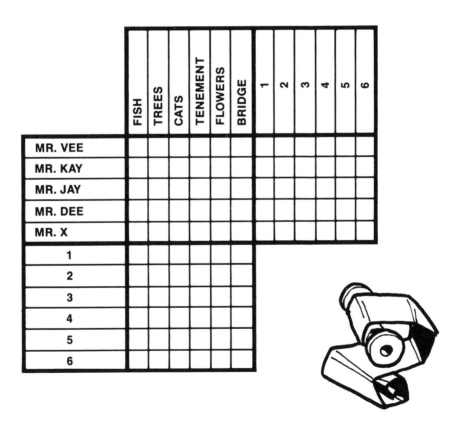

	FISH	TREES	CATS	TENEMENT	FLOWERS	BRIDGE	1	2	3	4	5	6
MR. VEE												
MR. KAY												
MR. JAY												
MR. DEE												
MR. X												
1												
2												
3												
4												
5												
6												

20. THE RUSSIAN COURSE

Edward, Mary, Robert, Howard, Harold, and Mabel are taking a night course in Russian at a university in Queens. They all come from Long Island but each comes from a different town: Huntington, Lake Success, Westbury, Mineola, Oyster Bay, and Great Neck. They are all employed—one is a broker, one an artist, one a doctor, one a banker, one an engineer, and one an editor. From the clues given try to determine where each person lives and what each person does for a living.

1. One of the women is an editor and the other one lives in Huntington.
2. The man from Oyster Bay, Mary, and the artist are all Harold's patients.
3. The engineer from Lake Success, the broker, and Mabel have plans to visit the Soviet Union soon; the others are taking the course as an intellectual exercise.
4. The man from Westbury, the broker, Robert, and Howard often make up a golf foursome.
5. Robert lives in Oyster Bay but he is not the engineer.
6. Edward and the banker often drive in to class together as do the men from Lake Success and Great Neck.

	BROKER	ARTIST	DOCTOR	BANKER	ENGINEER	EDITOR	HUNTINGTON	LAKE SUCCESS	WESTBURY	MINEOLA	OYSTER BAY	GREAT NECK
EDWARD												
MARY												
ROBERT												
HOWARD												
HAROLD												
MABEL												
HUNTINGTON												
LAKE SUCCESS												
WESTBURY												
MINEOLA												
OYSTER BAY												
GREAT NECK												

21. THE SECRETS OF FIVE WOMEN

Rachel, Lydia, Elvira, Kate, and Vivian, whose last names, in no particular order, are Parsons, Lawrence, Carter, Volpe, and Milligan, all live on the same block in Tinyboro. From the clues given, try to determine the first and last name of each woman and her age. The smallest age difference is 10 years.

1. Rachel's name is not Carter.
2. Kate is twice as old as Mrs. Milligan but only half as old as Lydia.
3. Elvira is 10 years older than Mrs. Lawrence but 10 years younger than Mrs. Parsons.
4. Vivian is 20 years older than Kate and 20 years younger than Mrs. Volpe.
5. Kate is 10 years younger than Elvira but 20 years older than Rachel.

	PARSONS	LAWRENCE	CARTER	VOLPE	MILLIGAN	AGE OLD			YOUNG
RACHEL									
LYDIA									
ELVIRA									
KATE									
VIVIAN									
AGE — OLD									
AGE — YOUNG									

22. DINNER FOR A FAMILY OF FOUR

A family of four—father, mother, sister, and brother—went out to dinner. They each had a different meat, potato and vegetable. The four kinds of meat were steak, ham, pork, and lamb. The four types of potatoes were baked, mashed, french fried, and boiled. The four vegetables were peas, carrots, corn, and spinach. From the clues given, try to determine the meal eaten by each member of the family.

1. One child had lamb and the other had french fries.
2. One of the women had spinach and the other had pork.
3. The father sat on the right of the person who had corn, who sat on the right of the person who had pork, who sat on the right of the person who had baked potatoes, who sat on the right of the person who had peas.
4. One parent had boiled potatoes and the other had steak.
5. One of the men had steak and the other had french fries.

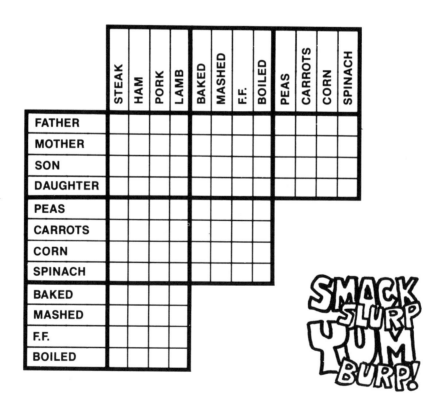

23. TWO-CARD HAND

Joe, Harry, Al, and Vince play a type of card game in which each player receives two cards. In one hand, each man received two cards in the same suit, and no man received cards in the same suit as any other man. The four suits are, of course, spades, hearts, diamonds and clubs. The first cards were an ace, a king, a queen, and a jack. The second cards were a ten, a nine, an eight, and a seven. From the clues given, try to determine the first and second card that each man received and the suit that both cards were in.

1. Al and Vince both have a picture card, and one of them has spades and the other the nine.
2. The man with the king does not have hearts or the seven and neither does Joe.
3. Harry does not have the jack or the eight.
4. Al sits to the right of Harry who sits to the right of the man with diamonds who sits to the right of the man with the queen of clubs.
5. The jack, the ten, the eight, and the diamonds are in four different hands.

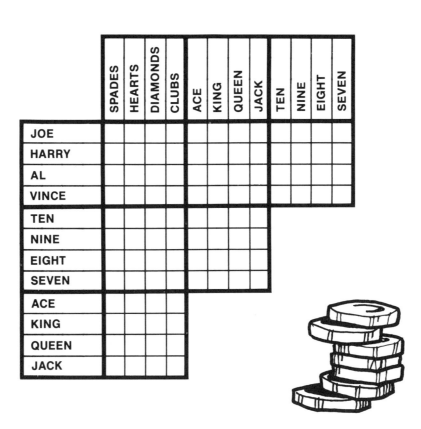

24. COLLEGE ROOMMATES

Five college seniors—John, Oscar, Earl, Ernie, and Marvin—rent an off-campus house. Each one is majoring in a different subject —psychology, chemistry, biology, math, or physics. They are attending college on sports scholarships in five sports: football, baseball, track, tennis, and swimming. And each is taking a different foreign language: French, Spanish, Italian, German, and Russian. From the clues given, try to determine the language, the sport, and the major of each of the five students.

1. The biology major, the swimmer, the student taking Italian, and Marvin have never missed any of Ernie's home football games.
2. Neither Oscar nor Earl is the one who takes Spanish or the one who is a physics major, but one of them is a baseball player.
3. Marvin and the track star had lunch with the math major and later on met Oscar after his German class.
4. The baseball player, the math major, and Oscar all have rooms on the top floor, whereas John and the physics major have rooms on the ground floor.
5. The psychology major is taking German.
6. The biology major is not the track star and does not take Russian.

		LANGUAGE					SPORT					MAJOR			
		FRENCH	SPANISH	ITALIAN	GERMAN	RUSSIAN	FOOTBALL	BASEBALL	TRACK	TENNIS	SWIMMING	PSYCH.	CHEM.	BIOLOGY	MATH.	PHYSICS
	JOHN															
	OSCAR															
	EARL															
	ERNIE															
	MARVIN															
MAJOR	PSYCH.															
	CHEM.															
	BIOLOGY															
	MATH.															
	PHYSICS															
SPORT	FOOTBALL															
	BASEBALL															
	TRACK															
	TENNIS															
	SWIMMING															

Five miners from Minnesota—Mike, Mark, Matthew, Malcolm, and Marvin—all man the same mine. Their last names, in no particular order, are MacNab, Miller, Morrison, Murdoch, and Meyers. Their wives' names, also in no particular order, are Mary, Mabel, Martha, Miriam, and Marcia. As it happens they all live on streets with names beginning with the letter "m." The streets are Main, Maple, Market, Mulberry, and Madison. From the clues given, try to determine each man's last name, the name of his wife, and the name of the street on which each couple lives.

1. Martha, Mabel, and Miriam play golf with Mrs. MacNab, but the woman who is married to Mark and lives on Madison does not play.
2. Matthew, Mike Miller, Marvin, and the man who lives on Madison played poker last night at Mr. Murdoch's house on Market Street.
3. Mrs. Miller, who lives on Main Street, and the woman who lives on Madison work with Mary in Mr. Morrison's office at the mine, although none of these women is married to him.
4. Mabel is married to Malcolm, but Miriam is not married to Matthew.
5. Miriam had dinner last week with the Millers and the couple from Maple Street.

	MIKE	MARK	MATTHEW	MALCOLM	MARVIN	MACNAB	MILLER	MORRISON	MURDOCH	MEYERS	MAIN	MAPLE	MARKET	MULBERRY	MADISON
MARY															
MABEL															
MARTHA															
MIRIAM															
MARCIA															
MAIN															
MAPLE															
MARKET															
MULBERRY															
MADISON															
MACNAB															
MILLER															
MORRISON															
MURDOCH															
MEYERS															

26. THE PIE CONTEST

Among prize winners in the pie contest at the County Fair are Mrs. Plumcott, Mrs. Custardine, Mrs. Appleby, Mrs. Peachet, and Mrs. Lemoni. In no particular order their first names are Janet, Lydia, Victoria, Vivian, and Doris. From the clues given, try to determine the first and last name of each woman, the type of pie she baked (custard, peach, lemon, apple, or plum), and the prize, first through fifth, that she won.

1. Mrs. Custardine's pie finished ahead of the plum pie which finished ahead of Doris's pie, but none of these won first prize.
2. Neither the peach nor the custard pie was baked by Victoria or Mrs. Lemoni.
3. Mrs. Peachet's custard pie received a higher prize than Vivian's pie which in turn did better than Mrs. Plumcott's lemon pie.
4. Mrs. Custardine's pie finished behind Mrs. Peachet's pie and they both finished behind Lydia's pie.
5. Lydia's last name is not Lemoni and she did not bake the lemon pie.

	JANET	LYDIA	VICTORIA	VIVIAN	DORIS	CUSTARD	PEACH	LEMON	APPLE	PLUM	FIRST	SECOND	THIRD	FOURTH	FIFTH
PLUMCOTT															
CUSTARDINE															
APPLEBY															
PEACHET															
LEMONI															
FIRST															
SECOND															
THIRD															
FOURTH															
FIFTH															
CUSTARD															
PEACH															
LEMON															
APPLE															
PLUM															

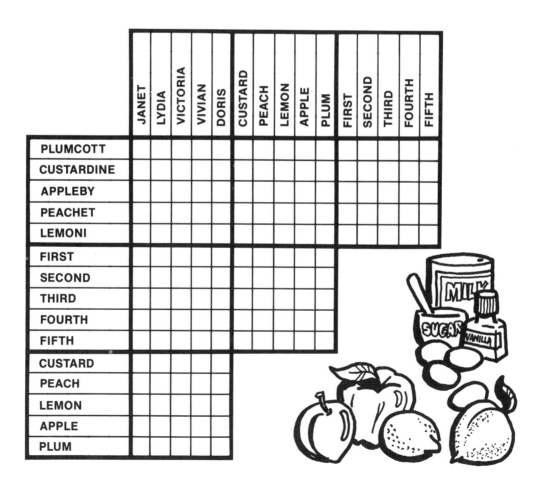

27. MUSIC POLL

Musicians Joe, Jim, John, Jake, and Josh recently finished in the top five positions of a music poll. Each plays in a different type of group—soul, jazz, country & western, reggae, and folk—and each performer plays a different instrument. From the clues given, try to determine for each position on the poll, the man, his type of group, and the instrument he plays.

1. The bass-player's reggae group finished third.
2. The folk and country & western groups do not have keyboard instruments in them and neither does Josh's group.
3. Jake's group placed higher in the polls than the bass-player's group which placed higher than the soul group but none of these groups finished first.
4. The drummer's group finished behind John's group but ahead of the jazz group; however, none of these groups finished last.
5. The guitar player's group does not play country & western.
6. Joe does not play his piano in the soul group.

		JOE	JIM	JOHN	JAKE	JOSH	DRUMS	GUITAR	BASS	PIANO	ORGAN	POSITION IN THE POLL				
												1	2	3	4	5
SOUL																
JAZZ																
C & W																
REGGAE																
FOLK																
POSITION IN THE POLL	1															
	2															
	3															
	4															
	5															
DRUMS																
GUITAR																
BASS																
PIANO																
ORGAN																

28. PARK STREET RESIDENTS

The Wilcoxes, the Byrds, the Talmadges, the Marsdens, and the Levers all live on the west side of Park Street. The numbers on the houses run from south to north, with the highest number being the most northerly, and only odd numbers are used on the west side of the street. Each house has white trim, but the main color of each house is different. The colors are red, brown, tan, yellow, and green. On the front lawn of each house there is a different type of tree in the central position. The five trees are an oak, an elm, an ash, a willow, and a maple. From the clues given, try to determine for each family the color of the house, the type of tree they have planted out front, and the address number of the house.

1. The Lever house is the next house to the south of the tan house and the next house north of the house with an oak on its front lawn.
2. The Marsden house does not have an elm in its front lawn.
3. Neither the Wilcox house nor the Talmadge house has a tree on its front lawn with a three letter name, but the colors of both of their houses are three letter words.
4. The green house is the next one north of the Marsden house, which is the next house to the north of the house with a willow on its front lawn.
5. The Lever house is the one just north of the green house and just south of the house with the maple on its front lawn.
6. The Wilcox house and the Marsden house do not have a maple tree on either of their front lawns and neither does the brown house.

		OAK	ELM	ASH	WILLOW	MAPLE	RED	BROWN	TAN	YELLOW	GREEN	9	7	5	3	1
WILCOX																
BYRD																
TALMADGE																
MARSDEN																
LEVER																
NORTH	9																
	7																
	5																
	3																
SOUTH	1																
RED																	
BROWN																	
TAN																	
YELLOW																	
GREEN																	

29. FIVE MEN ON SYCAMORE

On Sycamore Street, in a small town in Connecticut, live Joshua, Malcolm, Trevor, Rupert, and Charles. Their last names are Holden, Berger, Whittier, Previn, and Brooking. Collectively, they are graduates of Columbia, Cornell, N.Y.U., Harvard, and Yale. After college, they pursued the following professions: doctor, teacher, actor, lawyer, and veterinarian. From the clues given try to determine the first and last name of each man, his profession, and his alma mater.

1. Malcolm was not the one who went to N.Y.U. nor the one who became an actor; neither was his friend Mr. Previn.
2. Yesterday the lawyer, the doctor, Joshua, the one who went to Cornell, and Trevor Whittier had lunch together. There were five men at the table.
3. Charles is the veterinarian.
4. Neither Rupert nor Joshua is named Brooking or Previn and it was not one of these four who became a teacher after going to N.Y.U.
5. The doctor and the one who went to Yale knew Rupert before he went to Harvard.
6. Joshua is not Mr. Berger.

	HOLDEN	BERGER	WHITTIER	PREVIN	BROOKING	COLUMBIA	CORNELL	N.Y.U.	HARVARD	YALE	DOCTOR	TEACHER	ACTOR	LAWYER	VET.
JOSHUA															
MALCOLM															
TREVOR															
RUPERT															
CHARLES															
DOCTOR															
TEACHER															
ACTOR															
LAWYER															
VET.															
COLUMBIA															
CORNELL															
N.Y.U.															
HARVARD															
YALE															

30. PAULINE'S FIVE MEN IN EUROPE

All of Pauline's favorite male relatives live in Europe. They are her father, her uncle, her first cousin, her brother, and her husband. In no particular order, their names are Daniel, Edgar, Wilfred, Luther, and Walter. Although they all live in Europe, no two men live in the same city. The cities in which they live are London, Paris, Rome, Madrid, and Berlin. From the clues given, try to determine not only the city in which each man lives and his relationship to Pauline, but his occupation as well, be it diplomat, correspondent, student, artist or professor. Assume her husband is only related to the other men through marriage to her.

1. The man in Berlin is the father of the correspondent and the diplomat is the father of the man in Paris.
2. Luther is the son of the man in Rome and Walter is the artist's son.
3. Daniel is the father of the man in Madrid and Wilfred is the father of the student.
4. Her cousin does not live in Paris.

	FATHER	UNCLE	COUSIN	BROTHER	HUSBAND	LONDON	PARIS	ROME	MADRID	BERLIN	DIPLOMAT	CORRESPON.	STUDENT	ARTIST	PROFESSOR
DANIEL															
EDGAR															
WILFRED															
LUTHER															
WALTER															
DIPLOMAT															
CORRESP.															
STUDENT															
ARTIST															
PROF.															
LONDON															
PARIS															
ROME															
MADRID															
BERLIN															

31. JOYCE THE BABYSITTER

Joyce is a popular babysitter. Billy, Bobby, Sam, Tommy, and Pete are her charges, and she babysits for each one on a different day of the week. She takes Saturday and Sunday off. As it happens, no two children are the same age and range in age from one to five. The mothers of the boys are Mrs. Clark, Mrs. Jolson, Mrs. Prescott, Mrs. Foster, and Mrs. Waters. From the clues given, try to determine each child's full name and age as well as the day of the week on which Joyce babysits for him.

1. Thursday's child is the oldest and Mrs. Jolson's child is not the youngest.
2. She sits for Mrs. Foster's son earlier in the week than for Pete but later than she sits for the two-year-old.
3. She doesn't sit for Billy or Tommy on Monday or Friday but one of them is the one-year-old and the other is the three-year-old.
4. She sits for Tommy the day before Billy but the day after the Clark baby.
5. In no particular order the three youngest children are the Monday child, the Tuesday child, and Mrs. Jolson's child.
6. Mrs. Prescott's son Sam is not the oldest nor is he the child watched on Monday.

	BILLY	BOBBY	SAM	TOMMY	PETE	MON	TUES	WED	THURS	FRI	AGE				
											1	2	3	4	5
CLARK															
JOLSON															
PRESCOTT															
FOSTER															
WATERS															
AGE 1															
AGE 2															
AGE 3															
AGE 4															
AGE 5															
MON															
TUES															
WED															
THURS															
FRI															

32. RACE RESULTS

The first race at the Middleville Track was a five-horse race. The horses were Stillwind, Fleur-de-Lis, Graymere, Fool's Friend, and Emergency. The jockeys—Smith, Jones, Wilson, McCoy, and Larson, each wore a cap of a different color. One wore red, one wore yellow, one blue, one green, and one wore orange. From the clues given, try to determine the jockey of each horse, the color of his cap and the order in which the race finished.

1. Graymere won but was not ridden by the jockey with the yellow cap.
2. Stillwind finished ahead of McCoy's horse but behind the blue-capped jockey; however, none of these finished first.
3. Neither Graymere, Fleur-de-Lis nor Emergency was ridden by the jockey with the red cap but one was ridden by Jones and another by Larson and the other was the horse who finished fourth.
4. Fool's Friend finished ahead of the horse ridden by the jockey in the red cap, who finished ahead of McCoy, who finished ahead of the jockey with the orange cap.
5. Neither Fleur-de-Lis nor Graymere was ridden by Larson or Smith and none of these horses or riders finished second.

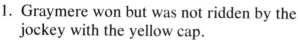

32

33. BIRTHDAY BOYS

Mrs. Smith had five sons, Norman, Felix, Raymond, Wilbur, and Edward. Each was born in a different year (1948, 1950, 1951, 1956, and 1957) and each was born in a different month (January, April, July, September, and November). Mrs. Smith remembers clearly that no son was born on the weekend but each son was born on a different day of the week. From the clues given try to determine the day of the week, the month and the year of birth of each son.

1. Wilbur was not the son born on Wednesday nor was he the son born in July.
2. Raymond is older than the son born on a Tuesday and younger than the son born in November, however, it is the two remaining sons who are the eldest and youngest.
3. The second eldest one and Felix both wear glasses but the son born on Friday, the son born in January, and Wilbur do not.
4. The son born in April was not born on Tuesday or Thursday and the son born in 1951 was not born on Monday or Friday.
5. The son born in 1948 was born on Wednesday and Norman was born on Monday.

	MON	TUES	WED	THURS	FRI	JANUARY	APRIL	JULY	SEPT	NOV	1948	1950	1951	1956	1957
NORMAN															
FELIX															
RAYMOND															
WILBUR															
EDWARD															
1948															
1950															
1951															
1956															
1957															
JANUARY															
APRIL															
JULY															
SEPT															
NOV															

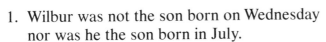
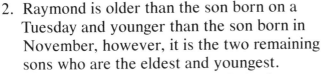

34. AT THE MOVIES

There are five movie theaters in Farville: the Strand, the Bijou, the Palace, the Capital, and the Odeon. Last week each one featured a different film starring the five favorite femme-fatales of Frankie (the film fanatic) Fusco. The five films starred Julie Christie, Bette Davis, Glenda Jackson, Marilyn Monroe (a revival film), and Katherine Hepburn. Each night during the week, Frankie went to see a different film. From the clues given try to determine the star, the theater, the type of film (drama, comedy, western, thriller, or mystery), and the night on which Frankie saw each film.

1. He did not see the western first but he saw it before the Marilyn Monroe film which he saw before the movie at the Odeon.
2. Neither Julie Christie nor Glenda Jackson played in the comedy but one of them was in the film at the Strand.
3. He saw the Glenda Jackson film before the mystery but after the drama.
4. The pictures at the Palace and the Capital were not the Bette Davis movie or the Katherine Hepburn western.
5. The mystery starred Bette Davis.
6. He saw the comedy before the thriller but after the film at the Palace.

	CHRISTIE	DAVIS	JACKSON	MONROE	HEPBURN	MON	TUES	WED	THURS	FRI	DRAMA	COMEDY	WESTERN	THRILLER	MYSTERY
STRAND															
BIJOU															
PALACE															
CAPITAL															
ODEON															
DRAMA															
COMEDY															
WESTERN															
THRILLER															
MYSTERY															
MON															
TUES															
WED															
THURS															
FRI															

35. LIKE-NAMED CATS AND DOGS

Joe, Bill, Bob, Jack, and Tom, whose last names are Carter, Dawson, Mingus, Wood, and Cole, live in an apartment building in New York. Each man owns a dog and a cat. The names of the dogs are Dusty, Midnight, Ginger, Smokey, and Daisy. Although the men do not know each other, it happens the five names they chose for their cats are the same five names chosen for the dogs. From the clues given, try to determine each man's first and last name and the names of his pets. (Hint: No man gave the same name to both his dog and his cat.)

1. Joe and Jack each have a pet named Ginger.
2. Jack, Joe, and Mr. Carter did not name any of their pets Midnight.
3. Bob's dog and Jack's cat have the same name, as do Bill's cat and Tom's dog.
4. The cat Daisy is not owned by Jack Cole, Mr. Mingus, Mr. Carter, or Bill.
5. Smokey the cat does not live with Ginger the dog, and neither of them live with Tom or Mr. Dawson.
6. Joe's dog is named Daisy.

		CARTER	DAWSON	MINGUS	WOOD	COLE	CATS DUSTY	CATS MIDNIGHT	CATS GINGER	CATS SMOKEY	CATS DAISY	DOGS DUSTY	DOGS MIDNIGHT	DOGS GINGER	DOGS SMOKEY	DOGS DAISY
JOE																
BILL																
BOB																
JACK																
TOM																
DOGS	DUSTY															
DOGS	MIDNIGHT															
DOGS	GINGER															
DOGS	SMOKEY															
DOGS	DAISY															
CATS	DUSTY															
CATS	MIDNIGHT															
CATS	GINGER															
CATS	SMOKEY															
CATS	DAISY															

Last weekend, the Carsons had a party and invited the O'Tooles, Levines, Jacksons, Martins, and Smiths. The five husbands were named Elmer, John, David, Charles, and Stewart. The five wives were named Mary, Hilda, Madalene, Jessica, and Marlene. From the clues given try to determine not only the first and last names of each of the guests but also the order in which they arrived at the party. Keep in mind that each couple arrived together as a couple.

1. When Mary arrived, her brother David was already there, talking with Elmer Smith and the O'Tooles.
2. The Jacksons arrived after the Levines but before Jessica.
3. No person at the party has first and last names beginning with the same letter.
4. Neither Hilda nor Mrs. Martin is married to David.
5. John and Marlene arrived together after Elmer and before Mary, but none of these people arrived first.
6. Charles is not married to Jessica.

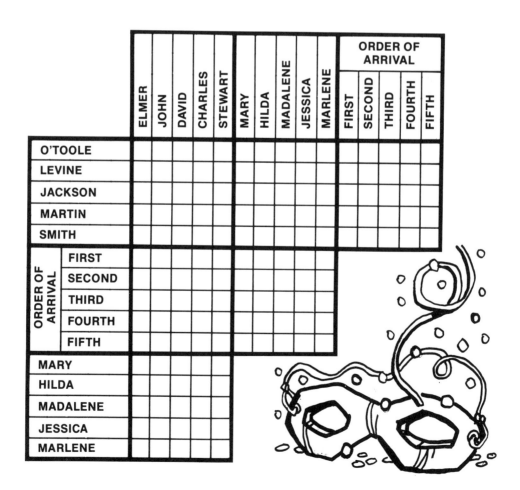

37. VITAL STATISTICS

Four men who work for the Littletown city government recently underwent their annual physical exams. The four men are Vince, Clem, Mort, and Phil. From the clues given, try to determine the exact age, height and weight of each of the four men.

1. Mort is five years older than the tallest man and he is lighter than the shortest man.
2. Clem is taller than the oldest man and lighter than the youngest man.
3. Phil is two inches shorter and ten pounds heavier than Clem but Phil weighs less than the tallest man.
4. Someone is 6′1″ and 40 years old, and someone is 5′11″ and weighs 170 pounds.
5. The lightest man is five years older than the shortest man.
6. The youngest man is 30, one inch shorter than Mort, and five pounds lighter than Vince.
7. The man who is 6′ is not Vince, 175-pound Phil, or the oldest man.

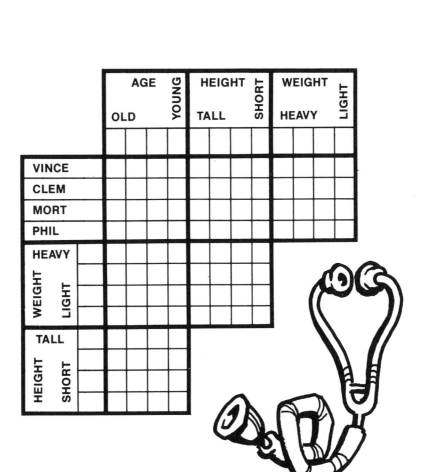

37

38. ANNIVERSARIES

On June 1st, five couples who live in Smallboro will celebrate their wedding anniversaries. Their names are Johnstone, Parker, Watson, Graves, and Shearer. The husbands' first names are Russell, Douglas, Charles, Peter, and Everett. The wives' first names are Elaine, Joyce, Marcia, Elizabeth, and Mildred. Keep in mind that no two couples have been married the same number of years. From the clues given, try to determine the husband and wife that make up each couple and the number of years they have been married.

1. Joyce has not been married as long as Charles or the Parkers but longer than Douglas or the Johnstones.
2. Elizabeth has been married twice as long as the Watsons but only half as long as Russell.
3. The Shearers have been married ten years longer than Peter and ten years less than Marcia.
4. Douglas and Mildred have been married for 25 years less than the Graves who, having been married for 30 years, are the couple who have been married the longest.
5. Neither Elaine nor the Johnstones have been married the shortest amount of time.
6. Everett has been married for 25 years.

	ELAINE	JOYCE	MARCIA	ELIZABETH	MILDRED	JOHNSTONE	PARKER	WATSON	GRAVES	SHEARER	YRS. MARRIED	
											LEAST	MOST
RUSSELL												
DOUGLAS												
CHARLES												
PETER												
EVERETT												
YRS. MARRIED — LEAST												
YRS. MARRIED — MOST												
JOHNSTONE												
PARKER												
WATSON												
GRAVES												
SHEARER												

SOLUTIONS

1. FIVE BOYS AND FIVE DOGS

Bart's dog is not called Bowser (Clue 1) or Rover (Clue 2) and he is not called Snoopy or Spot (Clue 5), so he is Fido. If Bart's dog is Fido, then Bernard's dog must be Spot, since by clue 3 one of them must own Spot and therefore, also by clue 3, Bart's dog Fido must be a spaniel. Snoopy is not Sidney's dog (Clue 1) or Eric's dog (Clue 4) so he is Ralph's dog, and since he is not a terrier (Clue 6) or a collie (Clue 5) or basset (Clue 4), so Snoopy must be a poodle. Rover is not Sidney's dog (Clue 2) so Bowser is, and Rover must be Eric's dog. Bernard's dog is not a collie (Clue 5) or a basset (Clue 4), so he is a terrier. Eric's dog Rover is not a basset (Clue 4), so he is a collie, and Sidney's dog Bowser must be the basset.

In Summary:

Eric — collie — Rover
Bernard — terrier — Spot
Bart — spaniel — Fido
Sidney — basset — Bowser
Ralph — poodle — Snoopy

2. FIVE WOMEN OUT TO DINNER

One woman had steak and corn (Clue 1). The woman who had squash did not have ham or chicken (Clue 2) and she did not have pork (Clue 3), so she had them with lamb. She was not Barbara or Gwendolyn (Clue 2) or Virginia (Clue 3) and she was not Elizabeth (Clue 4), so she was Gladys. Thus Gwendolyn had spinach (Clue 5), but she did not have chicken or ham (Clue 2), so she had pork. The wo-

man who had steak and corn must be Elizabeth or Barbara (Clue 5) and by clue 1 we know that she is not Elizabeth so she is Barbara. So again by clue 5, Elizabeth had carrots. She did not have them with ham (Clue 4) so she had chicken. Which means Virginia had the ham and peas.

In Summary:

Elizabeth — chicken — carrots
Gladys — lamb — squash
Barbara — steak — corn
Virginia — ham — peas
Gwendolyn — pork — spinach

3. PARKING LOT

The station wagon is yellow (Clue 2) and it is not owned by Mr. Jones or Mr. Brown (Clue 2), or Mr. Johnson (Clue 5) and it is not owned by Mr. Black (Clue 3); therefore, it is owned by Mr. Smith. Mr. Johnson owns a green car (Clue 5); therefore, he does not own the sports car (Clue 4). We know by clue 4 the sports car is not white, so neither Mr. Brown nor Mr. Black owns it (Clue 3). Therefore, Mr. Jones owns it, which means that Mr. Johnson must own the convertible (Clue 1). The sports car is not red (Clue 1); it is blue. The coupe is not white (Clue 3), so it is red. Mr. Brown does not own the sedan (Clue 2), so he owns the coupe, and Mr. Black owns the white sedan.

In Summary:

Smith — Yellow — Station wagon
Jones — blue — sports car
Brown — red — coupe
Johnson — green — convertible
Black — white — sedan

4. WHO DUN ITS

The corporal was not killed with poison, a gun, or a shovel (Clue 4) and not with a poker (Clue 5), so he was murdered with a knife. The captain was not killed with poison or a poker, (Clue 5) and not with a shovel (Clue 1), so it was with a gun. The general was not done in with poison or a shovel (Clue 4) so he was murdered with a poker. The lieutenant was not killed with a shovel (Clue 1) so the weapon had to be poison, and the sergeant must have been the one killed with a shovel. The sergeant, the captain and the lieutenant were not killed in the attic (Clue 1). The general was killed with a poker so he was not killed in the attic (Clue 3), so the corporal was killed in the attic. The sergeant, the captain and the lieutenant were not killed in the den (Clue 1), so the general was. The man murdered in the basement was not the captain (Clue 5) and because the lieutenant was killed with poison, it was not he (Clue 5), so it was the sergeant. The captain was not murdered in the bedroom (Clue 2), the lieutenant was; the captain was murdered in the pantry.

In Summary:

General — Den — Poker
Captain — pantry — Gun
Lieutenant — bedroom — Poison
Sergeant — basement — Shovel
Corporal — attic — Knife

5. VISITING RELATIVES

He arrived at his nephew's by plane (Clue 3). He did not arrive at his uncle's or cousin's by bus (combination Clues 1–2). He did not arrive by bus at his parents' (Clue 5), so he arrived at his brother's by bus. He did not arrive at his cousin's by train or car (Clue 5), so he arrived by motorcycle. He did not arrive at his uncle's by car (Clue 4), so he arrived by train; thus he must have arrived at his parents' by car. Because he arrived at his nephew's and his brother's by plane and bus they live inland (Clue 1) and his uncle and cousin on the east coast (Clue 2), so his parents must live in San Francisco. His uncle does not live in Boston (Clue 4), so he lives in Miami, and his cousin lives in Boston. Since he arrived at his brother's by bus, the brother must not live in St. Louis (Clue 5), so he lives in Denver and his nephew must live in St. Louis.

In Summary:

Plane — St. Louis — Nephew
Bus — Denver — Brother
Train — Miami — Uncle
Car — San Francisco — Parents
Motorcycle — Boston — Cousin

6. FAMILY AT HOME

A person is reading in the living room (Clue 1). Either the father or son is in the bedroom (Clue 2); one of them is in the den and the other is writing a letter (Clue 4), so one of the men is writing a letter in the bedroom. The aunt is not in the living room (Clue 3), so she cannot be reading (Clue 1). She is not in the bedroom (Clue 2) so she cannot be writing a letter. She is not doing the crossword (Clue 3) or watching T.V. (Clue 5), so she is on the telephone. She is not in the dining room (Clue 2) and not in the den (Clue 4), so she is in the kitchen. The son must either be in the den or the bedroom writing so he is not doing the crossword (Clue 6); so the daughter is. She is not doing it in the living room (Clue 3) or bedroom (Clue 2) so she must be doing it in the dining room. Therefore the person in the den is watching T.V. and this must be the father (comb. Clues 4–5) and so the son must be writing a letter in the bedroom, and the mother must be the person in the living room reading.

In Summary:

Father — Den — Watching T.V.
Mother — Living room — Reading
Daughter — Dining room —
   Doing crossword
Son — Bedroom — Writing a letter
Aunt — Kitchen — On the telephone

7. NIGHT CLASSES

Either Bernice or Pamela takes pottery (Clue 2) and it must be Bernice (Clue 5), so Pamela takes French (Clue 2). Bernice is not taking Italian (Clue 3) or Chinese (Clue 2) or German (Clue 5) so she is taking Spanish. Dorothy does not study German (Clue 4) or Italian (Clue 3) so she studies Chinese. Eunice is not taking Italian (Clue 3) so Rita is, and Eunice must be taking German. Dorothy must be taking graphics (Clue 5). Because Rita takes Italian she is not taking sculpture (Clue 1) or drawing (Clue 3) so she takes painting. Eunice does not take drawing (Clue 3) so Pamela does, leaving sculpture to be Eunice's art course.

In Summary:

Pamela — Drawing — French
Dorothy — Graphics — Chinese
Rita — Painting — Italian
Eunice — Sculpture — German
Bernice — Pottery — Spanish

8. FORMER HOMES

Mr. Lennox and Mr. Weiss have not lived in San Francisco (Clue 5), nor has Mr. Lester (Clue 2) or Mr. Standish (Clue 4), so Mr. Becket did. Mr. Lennox and Mr. Weiss did not live in Los Angeles (Clue 5), nor did Mr. Standish (Clue 4), so Mr. Lester did. Mr. Becket did not first live in Dallas (Clue 5) or Milwaukee or New Orleans (Clue 3), and he has not lived in Denver (Clue 2), so he lived first in Seattle. Mr. Lester who lived in L.A. did not live first in New Orleans or Denver (Clue 2) or Dallas (Clue 5), so he lived in Milwaukee. Mr. Standish did not live in Atlanta (Clue 1) or in Houston (Clue 5) so he lived in Boston. The first city he lived in was not New Orleans (Clue 4) or Dallas (Clue 5), so it was Denver. Mr. Lennox has not lived in New Orleans (Clue 4) so he lived first in Dallas and therefore also in Houston (Clue 5). Which leaves Mr. Weiss to be the man who lived in New Orleans and Atlanta.

In Summary

Lester — Milwaukee — Los Angeles
Becket — Seattle — San Francisco
Lennox — Dallas — Houston
Standish — Denver — Boston
Weiss — New Orleans — Atlanta

9. FAMILY WEDDINGS

Lester was the third brother to marry (Clue 1) and he is not married to Cindy Lee, Mary Jane (Clue 1), Betty Lou (Clue 2), or Sally Jo (Clue 3), so he was married to Peggy Sue. Leroy was either the fourth or fifth to be married (Clue 1), and by Clue 3 we know he was fifth to be married, therefore, Earl was fourth (Clue 1). Also, Virgil must have been first (Clue 3), leaving Ray to be the second brother to marry. Cindy Lee was married either first or second (Clue 1), but we see she was first (Clue 3), so Mary Jane was therefore the second one married (Clue 1). Sally Jo must be last (Clue 3) and that leaves Betty Lou as the sister who was married fourth.

In Summary

First — Virgil — Cindy Lee
Second — Ray — Mary Jane
Third — Lester — Peggy Sue
Fourth — Earl — Betty Lou
Fifth — Leroy — Sally Jo

10. THE LITTLE BIG TOP

The acrobat comes on third (Clue 2). The first performer is not the clown or magician (Clue 1). It is not the strong man (Clue 3), so it is the juggler. The strong man does not perform last (Clue 3) and neither does the clown (Clue 1), so it must be the magician who performs last. The clown does not perform second (Clue 1), so the strong man does and the clown must perform fourth. Since Victor and Vito cannot perform fourth or fifth (Clue 1) and they perform in the order Virgil, Victor, and Vito (Clue 4), then they must perform one, two and three. Vincent does not perform last (Clue 3) so Vance does and Vincent performs fourth.

In Summary

1st — Juggler — Virgil
2nd — Strong man — Victor
3rd — Acrobat — Vito
4th — Clown — Vincent
5th — Magician — Vance

11. A HEIGHT AND HAIR COLOR PROBLEM

The shortest girl (5'4") is not Mary or Ruth (Clue 1). It is not Isobel (Clue 5) or Marcia (Clue 3), so it is Grace. The second shortest (5'5") is not Ruth (Clue 4), because there is no 5'7" girl. It is not Isobel (Clue 5) or Mary (Clue 1), therefore it must be Marcia. The tallest girl (5'9") is not Mary (Clue 3), or Ruth (Clue 1), so it is Isobel. Mary is taller than Ruth (Clue 1), so she is 5'8" and Ruth is 5'6". Marcia is blond (Clue 5). Mary has black hair (Clue 4). Grace is the redhead (Clue 1). Ruth is not the brunette (Clue 2) so Isobel must be, and Ruth is the girl with the auburn hair.

In Summary

Isobel — 5'9" — Brunette
Mary — 5'8" — Black
Ruth — 5'6" — Auburn
Marcia — 5'5" — Blond
Grace — 5'4" — Redhead

12. FIVE DAUGHTERS' SONS

David and Malcolm were not born in May (Clue 2) and neither were Leonard and Harry (Clue 1), but Edward was, and he is June's son (Clue 4). Harry was not born in January (Clue 1) and neither were David and Malcolm (Clue 2), so Leonard was. Jane and Jean did not have a baby in January (Clue 3) and neither did Jill (Clue 1), so Joan had Leonard in January. By Clue 3, Jane had a baby in February and Jean in March, therefore Jill had her baby in April. Jill's son is not Harry (Clue 1) or David (Clue 2) because David was born before Harry and Harry was born before Jill's son, so Jill's son must be Malcolm. Since David was born before Harry (Clue

42

2), then David was born in February to Jane and Harry in March to Jean.

In Summary

Joan — Leonard — January
Jane — David — February
Jean — Harry — March
Jill — Malcolm — April
June — Edward — May

13. FIVE STREETS CROSS MAIN

The third street is River (Clue 4). Evergreen is not the first street (Clue 1) and neither is Oak (Clue 2). It is not Highland (Clue 3), so it is Northfield. Neither Evergreen nor Oak is the last street that one would cross (Clue 2), so Highland is. One crosses Evergreen before Oak (Clue 2), so Evergreen is the second street and Oak is the fourth, which means the Avenue is the last street (Clue 2). The Avenue is Highland. Evergreen is the Boulevard (Clue 1). The road is the third street, River, and the Lane is the fourth street, Oak, (Clue 3), leaving the Drive to be the first street, Northfield.

In Summary

First — Northfield Drive
Second — Evergreen Boulevard
Third — River Road
Fourth — Oak Lane
Fifth — Highland Avenue

14. COMMEMORATIVE STAMPS

The brown stamp did not cost the most (Clue 1) neither did the green one (Clue 2) or the blue or red one (Clue 3) so the gray stamp cost 25 cents. The red stamp costs 15 cents (Clue 3). The 20 cent stamp is the blue one (Clue 3). The brown stamp did not cost the least (Clue 1), so it cost 10 cents, leaving the green one

to cost 5 cents. The Wright Brothers are on the 10 cent brown stamp (Clue 2). The Marconi stamp is the 5 cent green one (Clue 1). The Franklin stamp is not blue or red (Clue 3), so it is the 25 cent gray one. The Edison Stamp is not the 20 cent blue one (Clue 4), the Bell stamp is, and the Edison is the 15 cent red stamp.

In Summary:

Marconi — Green — 5¢
Wright Brothers — Brown — 10¢
Edison — Red — 15¢
Bell — Blue — 20¢
Franklin — Gray — 25¢

15. FAMILY FAVORITES

The mother's favorite show is not on Monday (Clue 3), so the father's is (Clue 4); therefore, the mother's favorite show must be a western (Clue 4). It is not on Tuesday or Friday (Clue 3) or Wednesday (Clue 2), so it is on Thursday. Because the father's is on Monday the son's favorite must be on Wednesday (Clue 2). The father's Monday night favorite is sports (Clue 2). The drama must be on Friday because it is on later than the mother's show (Clue 3). The comedy is not on Tuesday (Clue 1), the interview show is, and the comedy is on Wednesday. The daughter does not like the drama and the aunt must like the interview show on Tuesday.

In Summary

Monday — Father — Sports
Tuesday — Aunt — Interview
Wednesday — Son — Comedy
Thursday — Mother — Western
Friday — Daughter — Drama

16. TWO WEEKS VACATION

The man who took his second vacation week in August was not Gardner or Plunkett (Clue 1), Lopez (Clue 4), or Maloney (Clue 5), so it was Phelps. The man who took his second week last was not Gardner (Clue 1), it was also not Lopez (Clue 4) or Maloney (Clue 5), so it was Mr. Plunkett, who did not take his first week in April or May (Clue 1), nor in January or March (Clue 4), so he took it in February. Mr. Lopez did not take his first week in April (Clue 3) or January or March (Clue 4), so he took it in May. Because Phelps had his second week in August, his first week was not January or March (Clue 4) so it was in April. Gardner did not take his first vacation week in January (Clue 1), so Mr. Maloney did, leaving March to be the month in which Mr. Gardner took his first week. His second week is therefore in September (Clue 2). Because Mr. Maloney took his second week after Mr. Lopez (Clue 5) he took his second week in November and Mr. Lopez had his second week's vacation in October.

In Summary

Maloney — January — November
Plunkett — February — December
Gardner — March — September
Phelps — April — August
Lopez — May — October

17. ROYALTY OF THE LAND OF PIRNZ

In Clue 2 we see that one person is older than, and two people are younger than, the baron, so he is either 35 or 40. His name is not Velve or Brint (Clue 2) nor is it Draz (Clue 3). Flard cannot be the baron because three people are older than he (Clue 1), so the baron is Sorn. Sorn is not 40 years old (Clue 4) so he is 35 years old. Brint is younger than the baron but not the youngest (Clue 2) so he is 30. Flard is also younger than Sorn (Clue 1) so he must be 25. At least three people are younger than the duchess (Clue 1), so she is either 40 or 50 years old, but she is not 40 (Clue 4) so she is 50. The queen is older than Sorn but younger than the duchess so she is 40. The 45-year-old duchess is not named Draz (Clue 3) therefore she is named Velve and the queen is named Draz. The 30-year-old Brint is not the marquis (Clue 5) so he is the duke and the 25-year-old Flard must be the marquis.

In Summary

Velve — Duchess — 45 years old
Draz — Queen — 40 years old
Sorn — Baron — 35 years old
Brint — Duke — 30 years old
Flard — Marquis — 25 years old

18. SPORTSVILLE TEAMS

We know that two teams share one stadium. One team is the Flames (Clue 1) and the other is the Streaks (Clue 2). The Flames must be the football team (combination Clues 1 and 2). The Fireballs are not the basketball or baseball team (Clue 3) or the soccer team (Clue 4) so they are the tennis team and they play at Memorial (Clue 5). Since the basketball and baseball teams do not share their stadia, (Clue 3) then the soccer team must be the Streaks, sharing their stadium with the Flames. That stadium is not Central (Clue 1) or All Saints (Clue 4) so it is the Coliseum. The baseball team does not play at All Saints (Clue 5) so the basketball team must and the baseball team must play at Central stadium. The baseball team nickname is not the Demons (Clue 1) so it must be the Blazers, leaving the Demons to be the basketball team at All Saints.

In Summary

Football — Flames — Coliseum
Soccer — Streaks — Coliseum
Baseball — Blazers — Central
Tennis — Fireballs — Memorial
Basketball — Demons — All Saints

19. THE PHOTO CONTEST

First determine who won the two prizes for the photographs of the tenement and the bridge which did not win first or last prize (Clue 1). It was not Mr. Vee, because his photo won first prize (Clue 2), or Mr. X, because his photograph was of trees (Clue 2). It was not Mr. Jay (Clue 3), nor was it Mr. Dee, because Mr. Dee's photograph is of flowers (Clue 4), so it was Mr. Kay who had two prize winners. Mr. Jay's photo was not of fish (Clue 5), so it was of cats, and Mr. Vee's first place photo was of fish. The photo that won third prize was neither Mr. Jay's or one of Mr. Kay's (Clue 3), and because Mr. Dee's photograph finished behind both the tenement and cats photographs (Clue 4) he couldn't have finished third, so Mr. X's photo of trees did. Knowing this and the fact that Mr. Vee's photo finished first, the only way for clue 4 to work is for them to finish 4-5-6. So Mr. Kay's tenement finished fourth, Mr. Jay's cats finished fifth, and Mr. Dee's flowers finished sixth. That leaves Mr. Kay's other photo — the bridge — to be the one that won second prize.

In Summary

First — Mr. Vee — Fish
Second — Mr. Kay — Bridge
Third — Mr. X — Trees
Fourth — Mr. Kay — Tenement
Fifth — Mr. Jay — Cats
Sixth — Mr. Dee — Flowers

20. THE RUSSIAN COURSE

Harold is a doctor (Clue 2). Robert lives in Oyster Bay (Clue 5) and he is neither an engineer (Clue 5), nor an artist (Clue 2). He is not the broker (Clue 4) or the editor (Clue 1), so he is the banker. A woman is the editor (Clue 1). She is not the man from Lake Success or Great Neck (Clue 6). She is not from Huntington (Clue 1) and since a man must be from Westbury (Clue 4), she must be from Mineola. Edward is not from Huntington (Clue 1) and he is not from Lake Success or Great Neck (Clue 6), so he is the man from Westbury. Since he is not a broker (Clue 4), engineer (Clue 3), or editor (Clue 1), he is an artist. The engineer is from Lake Success (Clue 3). He is not one of the women (Clue 1) and he is not Harold because Harold is a doctor, so he must be Howard. Harold is not from Huntington (Clue 1), so he is from Great Neck and the broker must be from Huntington. She cannot be Mabel (Clue 3) so she is Mary. Mabel therefore is the editor from Mineola.

In Summary

Edward — Artist — Westbury
Mary — Broker — Huntington
Robert — Banker — Oyster Bay
Howard — Engineer — Lake Success
Harold — Doctor — Great Neck
Mabel — Editor — Mineola

21. THE SECRETS OF FIVE WOMEN

The youngest is not Kate or Lydia (Clue 2) and it is not Elvira (Clue 3) or Vivian (Clue 4), so it is Rachel. The oldest is not Kate (Clue 2), Elvira (Clue 3) or Vivian (Clue 4), so it is Lydia. Vivian is 20 years older than Kate (Clue 4) and Elvira is ten years older than Kate (Clue 5), so Kate is second youngest, Vivian is second oldest, and Elvira is the middle age. We know that the smallest age interval is ten years, so we can determine that Mrs. Lawrence is Kate and Mrs. Parsons is Vivian (Clue 3). The only woman older than Vivian is Mrs. Volpe (Clue 4), so Lydia is Mrs. Volpe. Rachel's name is not Carter (Clue 1) so it is Milligan and Elvira must be Mrs. Carter. Lydia Volpe is 40 years older than Kate (Clue 4). That is twice as old as Kate (Clue 2), so Kate is 40 and Lydia is 80. Rachel Milligan must be 20 (Clue 2), Elvira Carter is 50 (Clue 3) and Vivian Parsons is 60 (Clue 3 or 4).

In Summary

80 — Lydia — Volpe
60 — Vivian — Parsons
50 — Elvira — Carter
40 — Kate — Lawrence
20 — Rachel — Milligan

22. DINNER FOR A FAMILY OF FOUR

One of the parents had steak (Clue 4). By Clue 5, it was the father. The son had french fries (Clue 5), so the daughter had lamb (Clue 1). The son did not have pork (Clue 2) so he had ham and the mother had pork. The mother had boiled potatoes (Clue 4). The father did not have baked potatoes (Clue 3), so he had mashed and the daughter must have had baked potatoes. The father had peas (Clue 3). The daughter had spinach (Clue 2). If the daughter had baked potatoes and the mother had pork, then the son had corn (Clue 3), leaving the carrots as the mother's vegetable.

In Summary

Father — Steak — Mashed — Peas
Mother — Pork — Boiled — Carrots
Daughter — Lamb — Baked —
  Spinach
Son — Ham — French fried — Corn

23. TWO-CARD HAND

Harry does not have the spades (Clue 1) and he does not have diamonds or clubs (Clue 4), so he has hearts. Al does not have diamonds or clubs (Clue 4), so he has spades. The queen is in clubs (Clue 4). The jack is not in hearts (Clue 3) or diamonds (Clue 5), so it is in spades. The king is not in hearts (Clue 2), so it is in diamonds and therefore the ace is in hearts, which is one of Harry's cards. The other is either the ten or the eight (Clue 5) and since he can't have the eight (Clue 3), he has the ten. Al so far has the jack of spades; his other card is not the nine (Clue 1) — that must be Vince's second card. It is not the eight (Clue 5), so it must be the seven. Joe does not have the king of diamonds (Clue 2), so he has the queen of clubs, and Vince has the king of diamonds. The eight remains, as Joe's other club.

In Summary

Joe — Clubs — Queen — Eight
Harry — Hearts — Ace — Ten
Al — Spades — Jack — Seven
Vince — Diamonds — King — Nine

24. COLLEGE ROOMMATES

Ernie plays football (Clue 1). Oscar is not a baseball player (Clue 4), so Earl must be (Clue 2). Marvin is not a swimmer (Clue 1) or a track star (Clue 3), so he plays tennis. Oscar is not a track star (Clue 3), so he is a swimmer, leaving John the one on the track team. Oscar takes German (Clue 3) so he must also be the psychology major (Clue 5). John, the track star, does not take math (Clue 3) or physics (Clue 4) or biology (Clue 6), so he must major in chemistry. Since Earl is the baseball player, he does not major in math or physics (Clue 4) so he majors in biology. Marvin does not major in math (Clue 3) so Ernie does, and Marvin must major in physics. Since Earl is the biology major he is not taking Italian (Clue 1), and neither is Marvin or Ernie (also Clue 1), so John is taking Italian. The student taking Spanish is not Earl or Marvin (Clue 2) because Marvin is the physics major; therefore Ernie is taking Spanish. Since Earl is the biology major he is not taking Russian (Clue 6), so he must take French. Marvin must be the student taking Russian.

In Summary

John — Italian — Track — Chemistry
Oscar — German — Swimmer — Psychology
Earl — French — Baseball — Biology
Ernie — Spanish — Football — Math
Marvin — Russian — Tennis — Physics

25. FOUR BY FIVE EMS

The Murdochs live on Market Street (Clue 2). Mark lives on Madison (Clue 1), so Mr. Murdoch is not Matthew, Mike, Marvin, or Mark (Clue 2). He is Malcolm and his wife's name is therefore Mabel (Clue 4). Because Mark lives on Madison, his name is not MacNab (Clue 1) and it is not Miller or Morrison (Clue 3) so it is Meyers. His wife's name is not Martha or Miriam (Clue 1) and it is not Mary (Clue 3), so she is Marcia. Mike's last name is Miller (Clue 2) and he lives on Main Street (Clue 3). His wife is not Mary (Clue 3) or Miriam (Clue 5), she is Martha. Miriam is not Mrs. MacNab (Clue 1) so Mary is, and Miriam must be Mrs. Morrison. Miriam is not married to Matthew (Clue 4), Mary is, and so Miriam must be married to Marvin. Miriam does not live on Maple (Clue 5), Mary does; then Miriam must live on Mulberry.

In Summary

Mary — Matthew — MacNab — Maple
Mabel — Malcolm — Murdoch — Market
Martha — Mike — Miller — Main
Miriam — Marvin — Morrison — Mulberry
Marcia — Mark — Meyers — Madison

26. THE PIE CONTEST

Mrs. Peachet made the custard pie and Mrs. Plumcott made the lemon pie (Clue 3). Lydia did not make the lemon pie (Clue 5), so her name is not Plumcott. Also by Clue 5, her name is not Lemoni. She is not Mrs. Custardine or Mrs. Peachet (Clue 4), so she is Mrs. Appleby. Mrs. Custardine's pie did not finish fourth or fifth (Clue 1), or first or second (Clue 4), so it must have been given third prize. Continuing with Clue 4, Lydia Appleby's pie won first prize and Mrs. Peachet's pie won second. Likewise, by Clue

1, the plum pie finished fourth and Doris' pie fifth. Since Mrs. Plumcott made a lemon pie, Mrs. Lemoni must have made the fourth place plum pie and Mrs. Plumcott's name must be Doris. Because Mrs. Peachet made the custard pie, Victoria's name is not Peachet (Clue 2) and, by the same clue, it is not Lemoni, so it must be Custardine. She did not bake a peach pie (Clue 2) so it must have been an apple pie. Vivian's name is not Peachet (Clue 3) so it must be Lemoni and Janet must be Mrs. Peachet. The remaining peach pie was baked by Lydia Appleby and won first prize.

In Summary

First — Lydia — Appleby — Peach
Second — Janet — Peachet — Custard
Third — Victoria — Custardine — Apple
Fourth — Vivian — Lemoni — Plum
Fifth — Doris — Plumcott — Lemon

27. MUSIC POLL

Joe plays piano (Clue 6). He does not play in a soul group (Clue 6) or a reggae group (Clue 1), and he does not play in a folk or Country & Western group (Clue 2), so Joe plays piano for a jazz group. That group did not finish first, second, or last in the poll (Clue 4), or third (Clue 1), so it finished fourth. The bass-player's group finished third and plays reggae (Clue 1). The organ was not featured in the folk or Country & Western group (Clue 2) so it was in the soul group. Because the bass-player's group finished higher than the soul group (Clue 3), the soul group finished fifth. The guitar player's group does not play Country and Western (Clue 5), it plays folk, and the drums must be featured in the Country & Western group. Since the drummer's group

finished behind John's group (Clue 4) then John must play guitar in the folk group which must have finished first in the poll. Jake is not in the soul group (Clue 3) or the reggae group (also Clue 3), so he must be the drummer in the second place finishing Country & Western group. Josh does not play organ (Clue 2) so he is the bass-player, therefore Jim must play organ in the soul group.

In Summary

1 — John — Guitar — Folk
2 — Jake — Drums — Country
     & Western
3 — Josh — Bass — Reggae
4 — Joe — Piano — Jazz
5 — Jim — Organ — Soul

28. PARK STREET RESIDENTS

The Marsden house is not red or tan (Clue 3), green (Clue 4) or brown (Clue 6), so it is yellow. The Lever house is not red or tan (Clue 3), and it is not green (Clue 5), so it is brown. The Byrd house is not red or tan (Clue 3) so it is green. The Wilcox house does not have a maple in its front lawn (Clue 6) but the maple is on the front lawn of either the Wilcox or Talmadge house (Clue 3) so the Talmadges have the maple, and the Wilcoxes must have the willow (Clue 3). Taking what we know so far, we can position the houses on the street. The most northerly house is not the Lever house (Clue 1). It is not the (green) Byrd house (Clue 5) and it is not the Marsden or Wilcox house (Clue 4), so the Talmadge house is number 9. Since the Talmadge house has a maple on its front lawn the Lever house is second from the north, number 7 (Clue 5) and then the Byrd (green) house must be number 5 (Clue 5). The Marsden house is number 3

(Clue 4) leaving the Wilcox house to be number 1. The Talmadge house is tan (Clue 1) therefore the Wilcox house is the remaining color, red. The Byrd house has an oak on its front lawn (Clue 1). The Marsden house does not have the elm (Clue 2), it has the ash. The Lever house has the elm.

In Summary

Number 9 — Talmadge — Maple — Tan
Number 7 — Lever — Elm — Brown
Number 5 — Byrd — Oak — Green
Number 3 — Marsden — Ash — Yellow
Number 1 — Wilcox — Willow — Red

29. FIVE MEN ON SYCAMORE

Trevor's last name is Whittier (Clue 2). He is the teacher who went to N.Y.U. (Clue 4), since it cannot be Malcolm (Clue 1), Charles (Clue 3), Rupert, or Joshua (Clue 4). Charles is the veterinarian (Clue 3), so he went to Cornell (Clue 2). Mr. Previn's name is not Malcolm (Clue 1). It is not Rupert or Joshua (Clue 4), so it is Charles. Joshua is not the lawyer or doctor (Clue 2) so he is the actor. His name is not Berger (Clue 6) or Brooking (Clue 4), so it is Holden. Rupert's name is not Brooking (Clue 4), it is Berger, and Malcolm is Mr. Brooking. Rupert is not the doctor (Clue 5). Malcolm is, so Rupert must be the lawyer. He went to Harvard (Clue 5). Malcolm Brooking, the doctor, did not go to Yale (Clue 5) so he went to Columbia and Joshua Holden, the actor, went to Yale.

In Summary

Joshua — Holden — Yale — Actor
Malcolm — Brooking — Columbia — Doctor
Trevor — Whittier — N.Y.U. — Teacher

Rupert — Berger — Harvard — Lawyer
Charles — Previn — Cornell — Veterinarian

30. PAULINE'S FIVE MEN IN EUROPE

In Clues 1–3 the sons mentioned can only be Pauline's brother and her cousin, while the fathers must be her father and her uncle. Her husband is not in Berlin or Paris (Clue 1), Rome (Clue 2), or Madrid (Clue 3), so he is in London. He is not Luther or Walter (Clue 2) and he is not Daniel or Wilfred (Clue 3), so he is Edgar. He is not the correspondent or diplomat (Clue 1), the artist (Clue 2), or the student (Clue 3), so he is a professor. Her cousin is not in Paris (Clue 4) or Berlin (Clue 1) or Rome (Clue 2), so he is in Madrid. Her uncle's name is Daniel and her father's name is Wilfred (Clue 3). Her brother is, therefore, a student (Clue 3). Her cousin is not the diplomat (Clue 1) or the artist (Clue 2), so he is the correspondent. Her uncle, then, is in Berlin (Clue 1) and her father must be in Rome. Luther is the son of the man in Rome (Clue 2) so he is her brother and Walter must be her cousin. If Walter is her cousin, then her uncle is an artist (Clue 2), leaving the job of diplomat to be that of her father.

In Summary

Daniel — Uncle — Berlin — Artist
Edgar — Husband — London — Professor
Wilfred — Father — Rome — Diplomat
Luther — Brother — Paris — Student
Walter — Cousin — Madrid — Correspondent

31. JOYCE THE BABYSITTER

Billy and Tommy are the one- and three-year-olds but Joyce doesn't sit for them on Monday (Clue 3), so she sits for one on Tuesday and the other is Mrs. Jolson's child (Clue 5). Mrs. Jolson's son is not the one-year-old (Clue 1) so he is the three-year-old. The child Joyce sits for on Tuesday is the one-year-old. She sits for Tommy before Billy (Clue 4), so Tommy is the 1-year-old watched on Tuesday, and Billy is Mrs. Jolson's 3-year-old (Clue 3), who is not watched on Thursday (Clue 1) and not on Monday or Friday (Clue 3), but on Wednesday. Since Joyce watches Tommy on Tuesday, she must watch the Clark baby on Monday (Clue 4) and that child must be the two-year-old (Clue 5). His name is not Sam (Clue 6) or Pete (Clue 2) so it is Bobby. Mrs. Prescott's son is named Sam (Clue 6). Pete's name is not Foster (Clue 2) so it is Waters and Tommy's name must be Foster. Sam Prescott is not the oldest (Clue 6) so he is four years old and Pete Waters must be the five-year-old. Pete must be watched on Thursday (Clue 1) therefore Joyce must watch Sam on Friday.

In Summary

Monday — Bobby — Clark — 2 years old
Tuesday — Tommy — Foster — 1 year old
Wednesday — Billy — Jolson —
   3 years old
Thursday — Pete — Waters — 5 years old
Friday — Sam — Prescott — 4 years old

32. RACE RESULTS

Graymere finished first (Clue 1). He was ridden by Jones or Larson (Clue 3), but he was not ridden by Larson (Clue 5), so he was ridden by Jones. The jockeys in the red and orange caps did not finish first (Clue 4). The blue-capped jockey did not finish first (Clue 2) and neither did the jockey in the yellow cap (Clue 1) so the jockey in the green cap was Jones riding Graymere and finishing first. Larson did not ride Fleur-de-Lis (Clue 5) so he rode Emergency (Clue 3) and therefore Fleur-de-Lis finished fourth (Clue 3). McCoy did not finish last (Clue 4) so by Clue 2 he must have finished fourth on Fleur-de-Lis. His cap was not red or orange (Clue 4) and it wasn't blue (Clue 2) so it was yellow. The jockey on Fool's Friend was not wearing a red or orange cap (Clue 4), so it was blue and he must have finished second to be two ahead of McCoy (Clue 2), and Stillwind's jockey had a red cap finishing third, leaving the orange cap for Larson, the jockey on Emergency who finished fifth. Since Smith did not finish second (Clue 5) he finished third and Wilson rode Fool's Friend to second place.

In Summary

1st — Graymere — Jones — Green
2nd — Fool's Friend — Wilson —
   Blue
3rd — Stillwind — Smith — Red
4th — Fleur-de-Lis — McCoy —
   Yellow
5th — Emergency — Larson —
   Orange

33. BIRTHDAY BOYS

Because none of the three people mentioned in Clue 2 is the eldest or youngest, we can determine that Raymond was the middle child (born in 1951), the son born on Tuesday is younger (born in 1956), and the son born in November is older (born in 1950). Norman was born on Monday (Clue 5). Raymond was not born on Friday (Clue 4) and not on Tuesday (Clue 2) or Wednesday (Clue 5), so he was born on Thursday. Wilbur was not born on Wednesday (Clue 1) or Friday (Clue 3), so he was born on Tuesday in 1956. Felix was not born on Friday (Clue 3), he was born on Wednesday, so Edward must have been born on Friday. The Wednesday on which Felix was born was in 1948 (Clue 5). The second eldest (1950) mentioned in Clue 3 cannot be Edward because he was born on Friday, so it must be Norman. That leaves Edward as the youngest (born in 1957). To determine the months, we know the son born in November was born in 1950 and thus is Norman. Wilbur was not born in July (Clue 1) nor in January (Clue 3), and because he was born on Tuesday he was not born in April (Clue 4), so he was born in September. The Wednesday on which Felix was born was not in July (Clue 1) or January (Clue 3), so it was in April. Since Edward was born on Friday he could not have been born in January (Clue 3), so he was born in July, leaving Raymond to be the son born in January.

In Summary

Felix — Wednesday — April — 1948
Norman — Monday — November — 1950
Raymond — Thursday — January — 1951
Wilbur — Tuesday — September — 1956
Edward — Friday — July — 1957

34. AT THE MOVIES

Bette Davis starred in the mystery (Clue 5) and Katherine Hepburn starred in the western (Clue 4). Neither Julie Christie nor Glenda Jackson starred in the comedy (Clue 2), so Marilyn Monroe did. The first film Frankie went to see was not the western (Clue 1) or the mystery (Clue 3), nor was it the comedy or thriller (Clue 6). Therefore, it was the drama. At the Palace, the western was not playing (Clue 4), neither were the mystery (combination Clues 4 and 5), the comedy, or the thriller (Clue 6), so the drama was playing there and it was the first theater he went to. The actress in this first film was not Marilyn Monroe (Clue 1) nor Davis or Hepburn (Clue 4), and it was not Glenda Jackson (Clue 3), so it was Julie Christie. Glenda Jackson, then, was in the thriller at the Strand (Clue 2). Monroe and Hepburn were not at the Odeon (Clue 1), so Bette Davis in the mystery was there. Katherine Hepburn was not at the Capital (Clue 4), Marilyn Monroe was, so Hepburn must have been playing at the Bijou. He did not see the Hepburn or Monroe films last (Clue 1) nor the Glenda Jackson film (Clue 3), therefore the last film he saw was the Bette Davis mystery at the Odeon. The second to last film was not the Hepburn western (Clue 1) or the Monroe comedy (Clue 6), it was the Jackson thriller at the Strand. By Clue 1 we know he saw the Hepburn western second, before the Monroe comedy.

In Summary

Monday — Julie Christie — Drama — Palace
Tuesday — Katherine Hepburn — Western — Bijou
Wednesday — Marilyn Monroe — Comedy — Capital
Thursday — Glenda Jackson — Thriller — Strand
Friday — Bette Davis — Mystery — Odeon

35. LIKE-NAMED CATS AND DOGS

Joe's dog is named Daisy (Clue 6), so his cat must be Ginger, and Jack's dog must be named Ginger (Clue 1). Jack's last name is Cole (Clue 4) and his cat's name is not Midnight (Clue 2), Daisy (Clue 4), or Smokey (Clue 5), so it must be Dusty. Bob's dog must be named Dusty (Clue 3). Since Joe does not own the cat Daisy he must be one of the four men mentioned in Clue 4. He is either Mr. Mingus or Mr. Carter, but he is not Mr. Carter (Clue 2), so he is Mr. Mingus. Mr. Carter does not own Midnight the cat (Clue 2) or Daisy the cat (Clue 4), so his cat is named Smokey. Mr. Carter's first name is not Bill (Clue 4) or Tom (Clue 5), so it is Bob. With the only name remaining which is common to both cats and dogs being Midnight, this must be the name of Bill's cat and Tom's dog (Clue 3). That leaves Bill's dog to be named Smokey and Tom's cat to be named Daisy. Since Tom's name is not Dawson (Clue 5) it must be Wood, and Bill's name is Dawson.

In Summary

Joe — Mingus — Daisy (d) — Ginger (c)
Bill — Dawson — Smokey (d) — Midnight (c)
Bob — Carter — Dusty (d) — Smokey (c)
Jack — Cole — Ginger (d) — Dusty (c)
Tom — Wood — Midnight (d) — Daisy (c)

36. THE PARTY

Madalene, Marlene, and Mary are not Mrs. Martin (Clue 3) and neither is Hilda (Clue 4), so Jessica is Mrs. Martin. The last couple to arrive was not the Smiths or O'Tooles (Clue 1), and it was not the Jacksons or Levines (Clue 2), so it was Jessica Martin who arrived last. Her husband is not David (Clue 4) or John (Clue 5; since no two couples arrived simultaneously, John and Marlene must be married) and not Elmer (Clue 1) or Charles (Clue 6), so it is Stewart. Elmer is Mr. Smith (Clue 1). He was not the first to arrive (Clue 5). Also by clue 5, because Mary and Marlene arrived after him, he must have arrived second. Then continuing with clue 5, John and Marlene must have arrived third and Mary fourth. Mary is not married to Elmer or David (Clue 1) so she is married to Charles. Hilda is not married to David (Clue 4) so she is married to Elmer Smith and Madalene must be married to David. John and Marlene arrived after Elmer (Clue 5) and John's name is not Jackson (Clue 3) so they are the O'Tooles. Finally, because the Jacksons arrived after the Levines (Clue 2), they are Charles and Mary, and the Levines who arrived first are David and Madalene.

In Summary

David — Madalene — Levine — First
Elmer — Hilda — Smith — Second
John — Marlene — O'Toole — Third
Charles — Mary — Jackson — Fourth
Stewart — Jessica — Martin — Fifth

37. VITAL STATISTICS

Clem is not the oldest (Clue 2) and neither are Vince and Phil (Clue 7), so Mort is the oldest. Clem is not the youngest (Clue 2) and neither is Vince (Clue 6), so Phil is the youngest. Mort is not the tallest (Clue 1), neither are Phil and Clem (Clue 3), so Vince is the tallest. The shortest is not Mort (Clue 1) or Clem (Clue 3), so it is Phil. Clem is taller than Mort (Clue 2), so he is second tallest and Mort is third tallest. Clem is 6' (Clue 7) so Phil is 5'10" (Clue 3) and Mort is 5'11" (Clue 6). Since someone is 6'1" (Clue 4), this must be Vince. Phil weighs 175 pounds (Clue 7), Mort weighs 170 pounds (Clue 4), Vince weighs 180 pounds (Clue 6) and Clem weighs 165 pounds (Clue 3). Phil is 30 (Clue 6), Vince is 40 (Clue 4), Mort is 45 (Clue 1) and Clem is 35 years old (Clue 5).

In Summary

45 — Mort — 5'11" — 170 pounds
40 — Vince — 6'1" — 180 pounds
35 — Clem — 6' — 165 pounds
30 — Phil — 5'10" — 175 pounds

38. ANNIVERSARIES

First determine the number of years each couple has been married. One couple has been married 25 years (Clue 6) another couple 30 years, and Douglas and Mildred five years (Clue 4). Douglas and Mildred's last name is not Graves (Clue 4), Parker or Johnstone (Clue 1). It cannot be Shearer because by Clue 3 we know the Shearers have been married longer than 10 years, so Mildred and Douglas are the Watsons. Therefore, by Clue 2 the remaining two anniversary years are 10 years and 20 years. Russell has been married 20 years (Clue 2) and is Mr. Shearer. Joyce has been married the middle number of years (Clue 1), so she is Mrs. Shearer. The Johnstones have been married ten years (Clue 1). Elizabeth has been married ten years (Clue 2), so she is Mrs. Johnstone. Peter has been married ten years (Clue 3) so he is Mr. Johnstone. Charles's name is not Parker (Clue 1) so it is Graves, and Everett is Mr. Parker. The Graves have been married 30 years (Clue 4) and Marcia has been married 30 years (Clue 3) so she is Mrs. Graves and Elaine is Mrs. Parker, married 25 years.

In Summary

Douglas — Mildred — Watson — 5 years
Peter — Elizabeth — Johnstone — 10 years
Russell — Joyce — Shearer — 20 years
Everett — Elaine — Parker — 25 years
Charles — Marcia — Graves — 30 years